BITS OF REFLECTIONS BY THE AUTHORS

I found it very therapeutic and empowering both to write and to share out loud. ... My classmates and instructor were so affirming about my piece and about me! Sharing encouraged me to continue expressing my feelings to the best of my ability in my freewriting, and later to finish my pieces at home.

Anonymous

Most importantly, we were encouraged to just write! I did not write "fancy" stories, but they are my stories and my family's, unique and different from the rest.

Stephanie Castro-Hernández

The best thing was being able to share [my writing] and get complements on the way I write. Sharing these freewrites helped me change and open up to people, I am a really introverted person but I was able to step out of my comfort zone and share my stories.

Suseth Fonseca

After re-reading my freewrites I thought, "Wow! I wrote that!" It amazes me that I can write something so powerful. ... I am very grateful for this class. I think every student needs to take a class like this, one based on freewrites, uncensored, and powerful writings.

Sarah Guevara

Another aspect that I enjoyed about the freewrites was being able to hear what others in my class had to say because I feel that it's really important to see how other people view things differently. Not only that, listening to each other's freewrites gave me the insight that although most of my classmates grew up in a Latino community or home, we all grew up differently while also sharing similar experiences.

Yanel Lázaro Cardozo

Pieces I wrote for this class are more personal and emotional than I have ever written before and it was cathartic. ... Being encouraged to explore writing styles and techniques, and just let myself use my most inner experiences as the basis for my writing was such a journey, and one I loved. ... It was so comfortable to know I could have a safe space to write from the soul, from my raw self.

Emma McCallum-Spalaris

[Writing] gave me an opportunity to think about the people who do relate to [different] prompts and how it affects their lives. [Writing] also brought to light my own intersectionality and strengthened my love for my culture.

Marlene Medina

I have grown as a writer, but also more of a wiser individual. ... Our stories should not be judged, they should be heard. We all have stories. Stories, that I believe we need to analyze and write about.

Guadalupe Reynosa

[Writing was] very liberating because there was no correct answer to the prompts. ... I learned things about myself ... and how the experiences in my life have shaped who I am today.

Christian Sánchez

Going into this class I wasn't expecting for it to be as healing as it was. ... As soon as my pen touched that paper, for those daily freewrites, all my anxiety melted away. ... Our stories deserve to be heard. Our struggles and our successes deserve to be shouted out loud into the ether. I will fight beside you to make sure our voices are heard, because tu lucha es mi lucha.

Marissa Lisette Sánchez

I want to thank everyone involved in this process, for finally including a class where I felt comfortable letting my stories come out. I never felt judged. ... I felt like I could express anything and do so in any way I wanted to. Thank you for the ... opportunity to write my very own CouRaGeouS Cuento.

Gabriela Emelyn Torres

I learned that I have a voice to be heard and I shouldn't be afraid to let it out. ... No one in class was ever alone, there always was someone who had been through a similar experience. We are all connected. I've learned to never be ashamed of where I come from and about my life's story.

Kimberly Vázquez

CouRaGeouS

Cuentos

A Journal of Counternarratives

A Journal of the Department of Critical
Race, Gender & Sexuality Studies

Humboldt State University
Arcata, California

ABOUT THIS JOURNAL

CouRaGeouS Cuentos is a journal that includes the creative writing of students in classes offered by the Department of Critical Race, Gender & Sexuality Studies. The journal is available both in digital commons at

digitalcommons.humboldt.edu/courageouscuentos/

and as a printed, bound copy available through Amazon.com.

The works published in this journal are by students in the *Ethnic Studies 107: Chican@/Latin@ Lives* class and students in *Ethnic Studies 480: Growing Up Chicana/Latino.* The students want to make their stories, their counternarratives, available to their families, their communities, and any other students who could relate to their stories.

The journal is published annually with the creative written works by students in the spring and fall semesters of each calendar year. The editing of the works is a collective effort through peer editing by students in the class, the student Teacher Assistant(s), Professor Barbara Brinson Curiel and the instructor of *Chican@/Latin@ Lives.*

Every student in the class has the opportunity to publish their work and do so on a voluntary basis. The students submit three pieces of writing and both the instructor and TA identify the strongest piece each student may, should they choose to, include in the journal. Some students submit more than one entry in addition to a reflection of their own writing process.

This journal is a publication by the Department of Critical Race, Gender & Sexuality Studies (CRGS) with submissions of creative writing works by students in Ethnic Studies courses at Humboldt State University.

Editorial Board

Department of Critical Race, Gender & Sexuality Studies
Humboldt State University
1 Harpst Street
Arcata, CA 95521-8299

ISBN-10:1-947112-00-7
ISBN-13:978-1-947112-00-1

ARTWORK

The hieroglyph (glyph) artwork was created by Michael Tjoelker, a student at Humboldt State University student in 2016.

The glyph is inspired by Nahuatl hieroglyphs used by the Aztecs in Mesoamerica. The single glyph, tlatoa, denotes speech, important speech, speech spoken by individuals who held social, political or religious positions of power and thus justified the writing of their speech.

This Journal reclaims the glyph to foreground the power of speech, the assertion that students already possess important knowledge, and the primacy of telling their cuentos--of telling their stories.

By orienting four glyphs towards a center we intend it to mean that the CouRaGeouS Cuentos in this journal are a form of a liberatory dialogue worthy of writing and publishing it.

Importantly, it is a conversation within community.

ACKNOWLEDGMENTS

As Editor-In-Chief, I wish to express my profound gratitude first and foremost to the CouRaGeouS students in the *Chican@/Latin@ Lives* class, Spring 2015, who envisioned the journal.

I am truly grateful for the CouRaGe of all subsequent students in the same class and the students in *Growing up Chicana/Latino*, who wrote their counternarratives and for the ones who submitted their work for publication in this volume. I want to express my distinct privilege in having the opportunity to learn with and from all students, in all the classes I have been honored to teach. You inspire me and fill me with hope.

My gratitude to my Teaching Assistants and later Associate Editors, Idette G. López Franco and Guadalupe Tinoco Oliveros, is endless. Their respect of the students' cuentos and commitment to the publishing of this journal are unquestionable.

To Professor Kim Berry, Professor of the Department of Critical Race, Gender & Sexuality Studies (CRGS), whose leadership and advocacy secured the approval from the College of Arts, Humanities, and Social Sciences for *Chican@/Latin@ Lives* class to be offered every semester since August 2014 and *Growing Up Chicana/Latino* starting in the August 2016. I thank her for her unwavering support of relevant curriculum for the growing Latinx student body at Humboldt State University, for her excitement about the journal from the very beginning, and for trusting me as we ventured on this amazing publishing journey.

To Professors Barbara Brinson Curiel and Christina Accomando for their generous guidance through the myriad considerations the production of a journal entails. Additionally, I am grateful to Professsor Curiel for her role as an Associate Editor and for her sage advice during our multiple conversations about teaching, writing, and editing.

To Cyril Oberlander, Dean of the Library, whose enthusiastic support for this journal first introduced me to the magical world of digital publishing. To Kyle Morgan from the HSU Library for his enduring smile and generous willingness to teach me and facilitate the digital publishing and hard printing of the journal. To Chrissy McGrath at bepress who made the idea concretely tangible and available worldwide.

To the student staff of the Latinx Center for Academic Excellence, for their excitement, for producing the promotional flyer and for expertly sharing it in the world of social media, a world still full of mystery to me.

To the Women's Enrichment Fund, the Latinx Center for Academic Excellence, the Office of Diversity and Inclusion, and the Library for sponsoring the printing of journals for students — ¡Gracias!

To the staff and faculty of the Department of Critical Race, Gender & Sexuality Studies for believing that our cuentos cuentan, that our stories matter, and even more so, they ought to be published.

For his sustained and personal support of this journal specifically, and of my work in general, I am deeply grateful to Dr. Noah Zerbe, Interim Dean of the College of Arts, Humanities, and Social Sciences.

¡Muchas gracias a todos!

María Corral-Ribordy
Editor-In-Chief

CouRaGeouS Cuentos
A Journal of Counternarratives

Volume 2   2017

COUNTERNARRATIVES & REFLECTIONS

xi

COLLECTIVE AFFIRMATION

Editor's Introduction

María Corral-Ribordy, Editor-in-Chief

Everything is contextual and this journal is no exception. The first volume of *CouRaGeouS Cuentos* appeared just six months ago, yet there is a profound difference in the socio-political context in the world since the inauguration of Donald Trump. Notwithstanding the record number of deportations that occurred during the Obama administration, Chicanx/Latinx communities tenaciously held on to the possibility that immigration reform in support of the legalization of people's immigrant status would be made into law. Young people still dreamed the Dream Act could pass.

Thousands of undocumented youth sought relief from the fear of deportation and applied for Deferred Action for Childhood Arrivals (DACA). With the promise of a temporary protected status, many unDACAmented youth enrolled in colleges and universities around the country. In California, these students can still pay in-state tuition at public universities as a result of Assembly Bill 540; however, they were still precluded from applying for federal financial aid to cover their educational expenses. Undocumented immigrants, many of whom are Latinx, held onto the hope, however tenuous, that a door of opportunity to legalize their status would open soon.

The unexpected election of Donald Trump, who opened his candidacy with criminalizing statements about "Mexicans," marks a crucial juncture in U.S. history. The current government is characterized by a Republican majority in Congress and the Oval Office staff ranges from ultra-conservative to "alt-right." The president already has appointed one Supreme Court Justice and likely will have the opportunity to nominate additional members of the Court.

Mexicans are not the only community that has been targeted as the undesired "other," deemed dangerous to the national security of the United States. The civil and human rights of women, Muslims, Arabs, Chinese, immigrants, political refugees, and all People of Color are under attack.

The xenophobic vitriol of the president, his immediate Executive Orders on immigration, and the increased funding for the Department of Homeland Security have resulted in a climate of heightened fears--of apprehension, detention, deportation, and other forms of violence by the state and vigilante groups--in Chicanx/Latinx communities. Raids, detentions, and deportations are already fragmenting mixed-status families. UnDACAmented students are very concerned about their future status given official statements that DACA will be terminated. What's more, the Department of Homeland Security will have a database with the personal information of thousands of young immigrants.

In these times of increased fear of escalating state violence, and the dominant discourse about who immigrants are in the imagination of mainstream America — Latinos, which is to say Mexicans, which is to say "illegals," which is to say criminals, which is to say rapists — that the counternarratives written by Chicanx/Latinx students are important, courageous, and urgently needed. This journal is intended to be a platform where such courageous cuentos can be published and made accessible to everyone who wants to read them.

This volume includes the CouRaGeouS cuentos written by students enrolled in *Ethnic Studies 107: Chican@/Latin@ Lives* and in *Ethnic Studies 480: Growing Up Chicana/Latino* at Humboldt State University in 2016. We have made no distinction between the students from each class because their writings are all, fundamentally, their counternarratives. The cuentos are organized alphabetically by the authors' last names. As a result there are clusters of topics that occurred by happenstance but also produce dynamic alignments and juxtapositions.

The writings reveal a mix of different languages, forms, and thematic content. The themes include emergent racial and ethnic identities, sexuality, gender identities, and self-perceptions as first-generation college students, scholars, and writers. The authors write of family and culture in complicated ways. Many write with gratitude and an awareness of the struggles their parents have overcome to provide the authors the opportunity to go to college and salir adelante. Other students write about the various ways their families reproduce gender oppression, homophobia, and white supremacist standards of beauty and worth.

Some authors have survived sexualized violence and others discuss mental health. In some cases alcoholism is linked with domestic violence. These testimonies are brave attempts to begin conversations to eliminate the cultural stigma and expose the myth that either "those things happen to other people" or "only I struggle with this issue."

A clearly salient theme for the authors is the importance of their own education: how pride and self-doubt impact their success; how, culture shock, sexism, and racism exacerbate their alienation at Humboldt State University; how the pressure to succeed and honor their parents can be a powerful source of motivation but can also be a paralyzing weight of responsibility. Many authors are grateful for their ancestors' struggles and wish to forge a path for their younger siblings and primx.

The Collective Affirmation is a list composed from students' assertions and affirmations about what they individually can do, think, know, and understand... This list was generated as a response to the dominant, and incorrect, perception that young people, women, People of Color, queer people and other marginalized peoples do not know, understand, do, nor can... Students submitted their lines voluntarily and the lines were sorted into different categories of assertions, mostly alphabetically. Different fonts have been used to highlight the individuality of each statement, however, there is no connection between fonts and authors. Though this poem's voice is first person singular, as a whole, it is a collective statement.

Students voluntarily submit their cuentos for publication, and some students also included reflections about their writing process and their experiences in the class. These reflections have been included to reveal the pedagogical power of creating a space for students to write/speak about their own lived experiences and the impact such process has had for their sense of self as writers, one which validates them as authorities of their own lives, and truths. Some excerpts are printed on the first page and back cover in order to illustrate the potential power of this form of pedagogy to liberate the students, in the words of Demetria Martínez, to name their own reality and "become a subject, not an object, in history" (Mother Tongue, 39).

By having students reflect on their experience writing throughout the semester about their own lives on themes connected to the curriculum they were studying, we can imagine other possibilities for unleashing their creativity. Here, the authors write their own stories, on their own terms — uncensored, multi-lingual, and with unflinching candor — the authors raise their voices both as a form of community building and in defiance, their resistance to dominant stories about themselves.

Martínez writes of the power of telling our own stories as, "Not psychoanalysis, [they are] testimonio, story as prophecy, facts assembled to change not the self but the times." (Mother Tongue, 32) The editors of CouRaGeouS Cuentos: A Journal of Counternarratives welcome you to Volume 2 and invite you to listen to the students-then authors-now prophets, who by using their voices and telling their cuentos, have in fact the power to change the times.

María Corral-Ribordy
Editor-In-Chief

Arcata, California
2017

Journal's Genesis

María Corral-Ribordy and Carlos Molina

"The Journal's Genesis" is an edited version of the "Editors' Introduction" from the journal's first volume. We are choosing to include it here because it documents the magical journey the students of ES 107: Chican@/Latin@ Lives class took in envisioning the publication of their written work.

That moment in class when students understand a new idea, one that illuminates their world a little more, one which allows them a deeper understanding of their lives--that moment--is sheer magic. We are lucky to get a glimpse of it when it happens, as if looking at the firmament and catching a shooting star off to the side of our gaze. For students, the moment excites them so much their eyes get big, they lean their bodies closer to the front of the classroom, slightly lifting themselves off their seats. We teach for those moments.

The genesis of *CouRaGeouS Cuentos: A Journal of Counternarratives* was one such event. The singularity of this moment is that it was collective and organic, a veritable meteor shower. It struck the students, as lightning making contact with the earth, full of energy, unpredictable, and powerfully beautiful—all at the same time.

This is how it started. In 2014 Humboldt State University had been recently designated by the U.S. Department of Education as a "'Hispanic' Serving Institution." Intending to meet the curricular needs and intellectual interests of a growing Chicanx and Latinx student population at HSU, the administration approved a new course: *Ethnic Studies 107: Chican@/Latin@ Lives*. Students read literary work by U.S. Chicanx and Latinx writers, and we discuss salient themes of identity, privilege, and the individual and collective resistance to the multiplicity of our intersectional forms of oppression.

Marginalized communities understand that language as a tool of power, thus language is emergent, in constant flux. It has the potential to be self-proclaimed and more inclusive of all the beautiful and complex diversity of the communities it attempts to describe. When naming the course we chose to use "@" at the end of the nouns Chicano/Latino as a way to challenge the Spanish language's patriarchal linguistic convention where the masculine noun can be used to label the whole community. The "@" symbol was intended to be read as an "a" and an "o," and include both the feminine and the masculine together.

Important critical interventions, however, have asserted that gender and sex are not binary categories. The traditional use of the masculine noun to also mean "everyone," renders invisible all people who are not identified as masculine or male, that is--all women, all gender non-conforming people, and people whose gender identity is not binary. This understanding has compelled the Latinx community to use language and be more inclusive by shifting the spelling from Chican@/Latin@ to Chicanx/Latinx. Using an x at the end of the noun honors and includes people who locate themselves at various points along the spectrum of gender identity while also including those who do identify as female or male. Everyone can be X. Though the name of the class is institutionally spelled with a "@," in this journal we will use *Chicanx* and *Latinx* to denote the singular or plural and inclusive sense of the words and their meaning can be understood in context.

In spring 2015, students of ES 107 were expected to respond to a prompt related to the assigned readings with a freewrite at the beginning of each class. The prompts were personal and sought to help the students make connections between the readings and their own lives. They were also broad enough to allow all students a point of access into the conversation, regardless of the constellation of their multiple identities. After fifteen minutes of writing students had the opportunity to share what they wrote with the whole class. Early into the semester, it was clear that students could not wait to write, could not wait to share, could wait to listen to what their peers had written about their dreams and hopes, the stories they survived, and the tales they hear and tell. With great courage, the students wrote about their always complex, frequently beautiful and often painful lives. The students showed kindness to their peers and affirmed the authors' strength and courage. Bearing witness to their peers' intimate and silenced stories cascaded into more and more students wishing to share their writings with their classmates.

A couple of weeks into the semester the students bemoaned they could not listen to more stories because of our limited time constraints. They paused, their lips slowly curved upwards. Corn kernels subjected to heat, their ideas and questions popped simultaneously. "What if... we post the freewrites on Moodle so all of us can read them?" "What if we make a pdf file that we share?" "What if we posted the pdf file on the CRGS website, on the internet?" "If we posted on the internet, everyone everywhere could read our stories!" Full of vigor, the students argued tenaciously, more accurately, they demanded that I help them share the stories of their lives--in their own words, in their own language(s), and importantly, in their own voice, en su propia voz — with the world.

They wanted to write for the whole world to read. They wanted their friends and family members to know--the ones who did not have the opportunity to pursue higher education--that lived experiences are factually valid knowledge. They wanted other students--students like themselves, the ones who got to college, perhaps one that is far away from home, the students who feel homesick before their families have the time to drive away--to know they are not alone. Ultimately, they wanted to speak for themselves, to challenge the stories about their communities spun by someone else. They wanted to tell it like it is, la pura neta. "Why not, María? Can we do this?" Inspired by their enthusiasm we said, "Of course! Why not? ¿Y porqué no?" ¿Quién dijo que no se puede? It was pura magia.

In doing so, we cracked a fissure in the ivory tower, the place where the worth of one's life is affirmed by the knowledge that is produced there; the place where such knowledge has not, until the last four decades, included the stories that resonate with the lived experiences of the majority of the students in the class.

Reminiscing about her writing during graduate school, one that eventually led to her writing of *A House on Mango Street*, a book the students read, Sandra Cisneros recalls,

> *I was trying as best as I could to write the kind of book I had never seen in a library or in a school, the kind of book not even my professors could write. (A House of My Own, 127-8)*

Literature by, for, and about Chicanx and Latinx lives is growing, and numerous authors have forged crucial paths of inquiry relating to the experience, status, and condition of our communities within the U.S. Our voices code-switch and the stories reflect the heterogeneous nature, hybridity, and complex history of Chicanx and Latinx in the United States. In our class, we read stories written by accomplished and eloquent authors, by talented and creative poets, and storytellers. These published voices speak to the experiences of Chicanx and Latinx students' lives. The voices that reveal the arduous trajectory from their barrios to college, and the insights into what it means to be a person of color, in a predominantly and historically white university, are loudly absent. The students of the *Ethnic Studies 107: Chican@/Latin@ Lives* class yearn to write such narratives; the kinds of stories that their professors, indeed, cannot write. We, the teachers of ES 107 wish to support their writings and publish them to boot.

On Language: The journal is a venue committed to honoring the authors' voices, language(s), and forms of expression and to recognizing their non-academic voices. The students are the peer-editors of their peer writers. The editors of this journal edited the work again, for clarity and consistency. In the Chicanx and Latinx community the issue of language is fraught with a sense of belonging, internal colonialism, and oppression. Following the U.S. invasion of Mexico in 1846, and the subsequent territorial annexation of the southwest, newly established institutions did not recognize legitimacy of Spanish. English was, and is, the language of the power--in the courts, in the schools, and the labor market. People of Mexican descent did not have access to jobs because they could not speak English. Spanish speakers were tried in courts of law where they could not defend themselves because the lingua franca was English. Children heard whispering in Spanish in the playground could be subjected to the violence teachers committed by smacking their knuckles with rulers. Worse yet, Spanish-speaking students were not receiving the full benefits of an education when the instruction was delivered solely in English.

In California, bilingual programs that sought to address this unequal access to education were legally dismantled in 1998, when 62% of California voters passed Proposition 227 in statewide primary elections. Wanting their children to have better opportunities, to experience less discrimination, to salir adelante, many parents chose not to teach their children Spanish. While Spanish language seems to be beaten out of our tongues, our communities include an ongoing influx of immigrants crossing the México/U.S. border, from all over Latinoamérica, assuring Spanish endures silencing, in our barrios, in our tongues, our music and our stories, alive and clear.

For these reasons, we deliberately chose not to translate, not to have a glossary, not to italicize--in order to avoid highlighting the preeminence of one language over the other. Then again, we retain the right to choose to do so, sometimes. Gloria Anzaldúa has named the borderlands as a place in-between, one that is much more than a geographic one, but also a cultural, historical, and linguistic one as well. She reminds us that we are a hybrid people, with "forked tongues," and who direly need languages that speak to our plural experiences. Thus, Chicanx and Latinx speak Spanish, English, Spanglish, Caló, Tex-Mex, Pocho, code switch and any combination of all of the above.

> *Until I am free to write bilingually and to switch codes without having always to translate, while I still have to speak English or Spanish when I would rather speak Spanglish, and as long as I have to accommodate the English speakers rather than having them accommodate me, my tongue will be illegitimate. (Borderlands, 81)*

Our purpose is to encourage the students write in their own voice, style and language; influenced but not directed by the diverse authors they read. In the process students reflect upon and articulate what is important to them about their own lives, in the context of the dominant narratives and counternarratives they analyze throughout the semester.

A central course theme is the importance of claiming one's own voice and the authority to speak. This journal makes this theme vividly real to the students. Importantly, this academic journal relies on non-academic voices. We feel strongly that retaining the language of choice of the author is the most inclusive way to articulate the contextual linguistic complexity among Chicanx and Latinx peoples.

El bautismo, the naming of the journal, was a series of deliberate choices. CouRaGeouS, as an adjective, it acknowledges the students' courage inherent in both the writing of their intimately personal stories and choosing to make them available to the world. Students are learning that stories create communities, offer perseverance and resistance, and at times, can save lives. The spelling of the CouRaGeouS, with specific letters capitalized, identifies the journal with the department where we teach and where the Chican@/Latin@ Lives course was created: Critical, Race, Gender and Sexuality Studies (CRGS). A Journal of Counternarratives explains what the journal endeavors to include: stories, based on lived experiences, that challenge, correct, amend, or complete the dominant narratives about Chicanx and Latinx communities.

Cuentos. Cuentos is the necessary Spanish word to signify the source and context of the journal's creation--the Chican@ Latin@ Lives class. Linguistically and semantically, cuentos is a tremendously versatile Spanish word. As a noun, a cuento is a "story." In the context of academia, personal stories, have not historically been recognized as important ways of knowing. Cherríe Moraga challenged that notion with what she called, "Theory in the Flesh" (This Bridge Called My Back, 25).

This journal foregrounds cuentos/stories as an important source of knowledge that the students already and uniquely possess when they first walk into the classroom. As a verb, cuento is the first-person, singular form of saying, "I tell (a story)." Yo cuento, is an emphatic assertion of "I am the one who tells the story, the story-teller." Cuento, as an intransitive verb, is a claim in first person that "I count, I am important, and I matter." "Yo cuento cuando cuento cuentos que cuentan, y mis cuentos cuentan" employs a variation of the word cuento six times, "I matter when I tell important stories, and my stories count."

This project closely mirrors the concept of Papelitos Guardados, which is introduced in *Telling to Live: Latina Feminist Testimonios*. The authors assert that papelitos guardados evoke the process by which we contemplate thoughts and feelings, often in isolation and through difficult times. We keep them in our memory, write them down, and store them in safe places waiting for the appropriate moment when we can return to them for review and analysis, or speak out and share them with others. (A Telling to Live, 1)

> *Through encouragement, the papelitos guardados are turned into Testimonios (shared stories); where reflection, healing and empowerment are borne through community engagement and support. Testimonio has been a powerful tool in movements of liberation throughout Latin America because they offer an artistic form and a methodology to create politicized understandings of identity and community. Within the classroom, students often shared how the literature and reflective assignments prompted them to critically reflect, often for the first time, on their personal identities, their communities, and the institutions they interact with.*

As editors and on behalf of the students of the Ethnic Studies 107 classes of 2015, we invite you to join us, escúchenos contar nuestros cuentos, listen to our stories. Welcome to the inaugural edition of CouRaGeous Cuentos: A Journal of Counternarratives.

¡Bienvenidos!

María Corral-Ribordy, Editor-in-Chief

Carlos Molina, Associate Editor

Arcata, California
2016

Counternarratives & Reflections

Post-Colonial Heteronormative Consequences In the Life of a Queer Chicanx

Armando Alejandre-Huerta

"Quítate esa putada y tirala a la basura." My mom was watching a novela lay across the couch. It was summer, but school was about to start. There was a silicone rainbow bracelet with the words "pride and joy" on my wrist. Her eyes only saw the colors, and her ears only heard 'lo que la gente va decir.'

"Pero sólo significa orgullo y alegría." I was ready to walk out the door, ready to leave no sé a donde, but I couldn't walk out the door without her permission. It was the summer of my freshman year. She wasn't working yet, so she was always home.

"Ay, tú no te ocupas do esas cosas," I heard this in the tone of her voice, so nonchalant, and I saw it in her eyes. The force with which she ripped that silicone bracelet from my wrist and threw it in the trash was full of hate! Honestly, that's not what hurt the most. What hurt most was having to accept her bendición, with tears in my eyes, before I left. I was mad. I felt defeated. She saw them, but perdóname is a word she does not recognize. The argument in its entirety is one I will never forget, and yet it's just one of those moments in my life that my mind constantly avoids.

I come from a world where we hide our rainbow bracelets. It is a place where I was only valued for being who I am not. It is a place that valued my image more than my reality, a place where labels could not describe me but only confined me. I come from a place that did not, and does not, value my story, my true story. Thus, my world has taught me that my story is one not worth reading.

I do not possess the power to control the negative and violent experiences in my life. As a queer, Chicanx growing up in East Oakland, I did not possess that power. Power is something I am afraid of because I've seen the destruction caused by the cisgender-heterosexual men with guns who have it. I have seen women in my life beaten unconscious and I was not able to do anything but wait until they woke up. I have seen lives taken and all I could do was avoid a stray bullet. I have escaped the violence when homophobia has been more than simply verbal degradation. Homophobia acted on by people within "my own community," the ones with the power to decide whether someone can take their next breath. A dim lit street and a gun can do that.

Oppression and injustice are not something I am new to. Living in a toxic environment, however, I was conditioned to accept them. I was forced to submit to and ignore my experiences of violence because, as a queer person of color, heteronormativity silenced my voice. I could not challenge the narrative in my own life because I did not possess the pen to rewrite it; that too, was taken from me.

Growing up, being identified and perceived as a Mexican male in East Oakland is difficult. I lived in an environment where systemic racism and institutionalized oppression railed against me. La raza y familia claim to be a source of support, one that empowers and motivates you to do better for yourself and improve your community if, and only if, your gender and sexual identity conform to their expectations. Growing up as a non-binary, male-identified, queer Chicanx in East Oakland exposed me to the same oppressive institutions, but there was no raza, no familia for me. Instead, I was, and am, devalued for not fitting the community's standard of normalcy. I was forced to suppress my identity to fit in with the community that openly despised my queer "otherness".

My parents did all they could to keep my siblings and I safe in Oakland. Safe from the risk of becoming another bloody body on the streets, but importantly, safe from other people's judgments. ¿Qué va decir la gente? They created a reputation, an image of me that they value more than the real me. My parents came to the United States to provide their children with opportunities that would not have been accessible to us in Mexico. They are incredibly supportive of the effort my siblings and I make in obtaining a higher education. We fulfill their American Dream. The one image of me they do uphold is one that solely depicts my academic "success." However, the one aspect of me that they do not support, that they hardly acknowledge, is a critical aspect that makes me who I am--my queer identity. The comfort, care, and support that other people of color experience within their families are ones I am not familiar with. Not having a home within my own immediate family, I was forced to create a home away from home, among people who are not my family, yet they accept and embrace my multiple identities.

I have a unique perspective of "comunidad" and "familía" than the one experienced by other people of my raza. As a result of the violent invisibility and ostracism from "mi gente," I do not fully embrace Chincanx as a core identity. I can more easily identify with people who have been marginalized by their own racial communities for their queer "otherness." If I had not created a sense of community among people who share my gendered experiences, beyond my appearance, I could have easily become another statistic. Another name turned into a number; a life lost among a list of lives that could have mattered. Another life, another smile, stolen and consumed by hatred. I am not a number because, subconsciously, I knew that one day I would be able to escape the smog of Oakland, and finally freely breathe.

Habla Ahora o Calla Para Siempre

Anonymous

One always hears and talks about sexual abuse but one never knows what to do when it happens. The molestation and the abuse that someone has to survive has been one of the biggest secrets I have carried with me for a very long time. Someone very close to my heart was molested by her father and had not spoken about it. Finally, she decided to tell me what had happened.

Weeks passed after her confession and we went to her family party together. During the party, her mom found out her dad was doing drugs with a friend he had invited. Her mom kicked everyone out of her house. We were all surprised and did not know how to react. All you could hear in the background was, "¡Maldito! ¡No me eches mentiras y vete de esta casa!" Her mom was throwing plates, cups, and anything she could grab and throw. Her dad got upset, and pushed her mom to the floor. Everything happened so fast. I heard in the background, "You molested me, I hate you!" She had spoken up! She openly accused him of molesting her.

It was as though she had whispered because at that moment no one acknowledged what she had just said. She must have felt like she had no voice and that she did not matter. I wasn't the only one, however, to hear her words. I saw her father's reaction. He acted like she didn't say anything and he ignored her. Her mom didn't hear her because she was too busy yelling, throwing things, and trying to fight him.

She started crying and went outside. I didn't have any words to say so I just let her cry in my arms. Her dad walked out, he looked at her, and then looked at me. He knew I knew and did not bother saying anything. After her dad left, her mom came outside and said that she needed to talk to her in the other room. Her cousins had heard what she said and told her mom. Not long after I got called into her room. As soon as I walked in, she ran to me and started crying, her mom was crying as well. Her mom looked at me and told me to tell her that the claims of the abuse were not true. I felt anger and I felt pity, her mom really wanted this to be a lie. I couldn't understand why she wanted to believe that her daughter was lying, that her dad did not molest her. I decided to speak up. I told her mom to leave her alone and to go to sleep because it had been a long night.

The next morning her mom came into the room and asked once again if it was true. The daughter cried and said, "¿Tu crees que lo voy a inventar? ¡Vete con él si quieres!" Her mom got mad and slammed the door. I went out to get breakfast and when I came back I found her on the floor of her bathroom crying. I asked her what happened. Her brother had told her that he hated her because she had just ruined their family.

She couldn't stop blaming herself for what had happened. I burst into tears because I could feel her pain. Her mom and her brother were blaming the victim and that was not okay. I told her it was all going to be okay without realizing that everything was falling apart. At the end of the day I left her house and went home.

The next morning she didn't show up to school and I decided to ditch and go find out where she was. I went to her house and when I walked in I saw she was alone, getting high. She looked at me, she was laughing with tears. I was not sure what was going on. She said, "My mom got what she wanted. I told her I was lying and then she left to apologize to my dad." I asked why she had lied. She cried and said because that's what her mom wanted. I felt hurt. I felt like she was unprotected. I wanted to take her home with me but that would not have been the best idea.

Her dad came home that day. To this day I have not asked her how she felt once her father returned. I haven't asked if she is scared. I haven't asked if she wants to go to therapy. On the surface she seems okay, as a matter of fact, she looks like there is nothing wrong, like nothing ever happened to her. But I know she will never forget June 21, 2014 because I certainly will never forget that day either.

My "Otherness"

Anonymous

The first time I felt my "otherness" was when my parents got divorced, I was five years old. I didn't have a mother in my home any more. Children I knew had a mother in their home. Some of them didn't have a dad, but at least they had a mom. Once, in first grade, we had to draw a picture of our family. After we finished our pictures, the teacher would come around to each desk and write each family member's name under the figure. I drew a dad, a mom, and all the children in my family, just like the other children in my class did. When the teacher came to my desk and saw my picture, she pointed to the adult female figure and said, "Who's that? It's supposed to be your family. Your mother doesn't live with you." So I quickly said the name of the housekeeper/babysitter my father was thinking of hiring. But I felt embarrassed and realized how different I was from the other students.

I felt "otherness" again when I had to wear special orthopedic shoes that were ugly because I had something wrong with my feet. Once, I was with my sister and someone asked me why I had to wear those shoes. I made up a story and said that one time I had broken my leg and it hadn't healed right, so I had to wear special shoes. Later in life, my sister said she felt bad for me that I had to make up that story and felt very protective of me even though she was younger.

My current "otherness" is that I'm queer. Since that is a "hidden" status unless I choose to share it, I haven't had to deal with many negative experiences related to that. People have asked me through the years if I am married or have ever been married. A woman I hadn't seen since high school asked me about my marital status. I told her I was not married. She quickly replied, "That's okay," but I knew it wasn't. It was as if she was trying to reassure me that she liked me even though she thought I am so "odd."

REFLECTION

Writing these pieces during class was an incredible experience. It was unlike any other assignment I have ever undertaken. Since the pieces were freewrites and were aimed to elicit our authentic voices, we had to keep our pens moving the whole time even if we just wrote, "I don't know what to write." At first I was very apprehensive as to whether I would be able to write anything coherent or if I would end up writing, "I don't know what to write," and "The weather sure is nice today," over and over again. But once I started writing, I found that most of the time the thoughts about the topic just flowed from my mind onto the paper. Surprisingly, I really did have a lot to say about most of the topics!

After each period of freewriting, we were given the opportunity to read the piece we had written to the class--if we wanted to. Listening to and sharing each other's writing was one of the parts of the class that, to me, built most the sense of community I felt with my fellow students. This was where I was able to learn about Latina/Chicano lives in an up close and personal way as most of the students identify as Latinas/Chicanos.

Even though I don't identify as Latina, the topics assigned were broad enough that I was also able to express my own experiences. On two different occasions, I chose to share my writing. The first freewrite I shared was with my piece titled "My Otherness." I hadn't finished it yet, but I read about the experience in first grade with my teacher's thoughtless remarks and how they made me feel embarrassed and "othered."

I found it very therapeutic and empowering both to write about it and to share it out loud. I hadn't thought about that period of my life for a long time. My classmates and instructor were so affirming about my piece and about me! Sharing encouraged me to continue expressing my feelings to the best of my ability in my freewriting and later to finish my pieces at home.

The second piece I chose to share with my classmates was my piece called "The Secret." Since it was about someone else's secret, I chose not to turn that one in for possible publication. But while I was writing it, I found tears flowing down my face. This was another thing that I had never experienced while writing. I cried again while reading the piece out loud to my classmates and instructor and could barely finish reading it. Again, my classmates and instructor affirmed me, making me feel cared for and empathized with as I made myself vulnerable and re-experienced the pain from that experience.

I felt like a real writer who could get people to feel something I had felt during a difficult experience in my life! Later I chose to share this piece with a counselor and discuss my feelings with her, but it was not as powerful as writing it and sharing it with my ES 107 community.

Secreto o Condena?

Anonymous

I can't say I remember the exact moment I realized I was different. I don't remember being in the playground and realizing I was looking at girls the same way I looked at boys. I don't remember having some crazy revelation like in a dream or a tarot card reading. I didn't encounter an old witch in the middle of the woods who gave me a poisoned apple and told me I was gay. My awareness of it was just always there, in the back of my mind. But as I grew up, and overheard the homophobia and flat out ignorance in my community, I realized I was different. It wasn't some big revelation, instead it felt more like blocks of Jenga being taken out of my life until one day the entire tower toppled over me.

I've always known my parents were homophobic, but it wasn't until their hate was directed towards me that I knew I was an "other." Hearing my own mother sigh or get disappointed as soon as she finds out someone she knows is gay always causes a sinking feeling in my chest. Knowing that she'll never really know all of me--and if she ever does, that she probably won't accept me--is a pain sometimes I don't think I will be able to handle. I love my mother so much, and I don't want our relationship to change over something I can't change about myself, something I don't want to change about myself. I'm not broken or damaged. I am not less than others. I wish my family and my community could see that. Being a Latina woman means I am expected to live up to certain expectations. I'm expected to be a good cook and take care of others. I'm expected to raise a family and become a self-sacrificing mother.

I love kids but I don't want any of my own. And I have no way of knowing if the person I'll end up falling in love with will fit in the traditional heteronormative box society puts us in. My biggest hope is that one day, our community as a whole will understand

and respect queer people. I wish the gay couples back home wouldn't have to be careful of how they act in public. I wish people wouldn't make homophobic slurs as a way to put others down. I pray my mother and father realize that I will still be the same daughter they know and love, even if I'm standing next to another woman at the altar.

REFLECTION

This freewrite was very hard to write because I had to tap into areas of my life that I don't like thinking about. Since coming to Humboldt I've grown more comfortable in my own skin and I've learned to love and accept myself in ways I never have before. I know that when I go home, however, I won't be as comfortable as I am here. I know that people will give me dirty looks if I walk down the street holding the hand of another girl. I know that I'll be treated differently if I tell my family, because they are extremely religious, especially my grandmother. I worry constantly that I'll either have to hide that side of myself forever or that, if I tell them, they'll look at me as if I were a leper. It's extremely hard to convince myself that what my community thinks about people like me isn't true.

When writing this, I thought about what it would be like to tell my mother. I started crying because I don't want my relationship with her to change. I don't want my mother to look at me with pity because she thinks being gay is some kind of disadvantage. I wish she could understand that I love her and that I just want to be myself. I know this is a fear many Latinx/Chicanx people face because of the deep-rooted fear and hatred that often stems from religion and machismo. Although there are other gay people in my family, it has taken the rest of the family years to accept them and be okay with it. I wish I didn't have to go through a process of worrying if who I love is going to offend my family. I wish my own happiness was enough to make them understand.

To you

Anonymous

I don't remember you. The only reason I know what you look like is because grandma still has your portrait hanging over the fireplace. But you visit me in my dreams. Every time you do, the image of you holding my hand as we walk together lingers in my mind for days. I know you didn't mean to go so soon and it's okay. Although you haven't been able to accompany me on this journey we like to call life, you've been in my heart. You don't have to worry anymore. I'm safe when I sleep. I love you.

I think one day I'll paint that image. I'll make it really pretty and hang it over my own fireplace so that everyone can see what I see when you come to visit me. Ariel says I look like you more and more every time he sees me. I wouldn't know, but I'm glad I look like you. Tony has raised me well, with lots of love and compassion, like I know you would have. I'm in college now, but no matter how busy I get, I never forget you. I hope you're proud of me. You don't have to worry anymore. I'm safe when I sleep.

I love you.

REFLECTION

The first time we were instructed to do a freewrite my brain went blank. I was so flustered and I couldn't even begin writing because I hadn't really done that in a while. Luckily for me though, I enjoy writing. I really enjoy finding words and phrases that capture what I'm feeling or trying to portray. So when I became aware that every day in class we would dedicate a certain amount of time to just that, I was excited!

The prompts we were given each time forced me to think not only about my own experiences but also about the Chicano experience. The instructor does a great job by building-up to the freewrites with background information or by personalizing the readings. The stage is then set for an amazing outburst of passion expressed with a pen and paper backed by knowledge of the history of our own lives and of our people. There were days when I liked the prompts and days when I kind of just wrote to write, but all in all, if it wasn't for the freewrites and having to reach into my bag of experiences, opinions and beliefs, I do not believe I would have fully grasped many of the common themes discussed in class about Chican@/Latin@ Lives. Most importantly, if it had not been for the freewrites, I don't believe that I would have made the multiple connections in relevant aspects of my own life.

I Was Named After My Father

Hector Alejandro Arzate

My name is Hector Alejandro Arzate.

I was named after my father, but I don't know why. My name was important the day that I was born. But unlike most other boys named after their dad, I was not the first born son. I am the fourth child, and every day I have wondered why I was given this name. In search of answers, I have allowed my imagination run. Perhaps my brother, Luis, was not named Alejandro because my father did not think it would suit him. Or maybe my sister, Alejandra, was close but not close enough. Maybe it was no longer important to him when Juan was born. I imagine that my father stopped thinking about passing his name onto his sons until my mom found out she was pregnant with me. Maybe it was then that he felt the need to take advantage of this new opportunity.

In the end, I do not think it was as important to him as it was to me. I wanted to know what his reasoning was, but he never told me. Not even when he left. From him, there was no inheritance of warmth or wisdom, no memories of being a son or having a father. I only felt hate for him, every day, whenever someone called my name. Of all things, why would he leave me with his name? I do not think he will ever answer me. I will make sense and meaning of my name, and importantly, of who I want to be in this world--on my own. My name means love and grace; today as a son and some day as a father.

My name is Hector Alejandro Arzate.

I was named after my father.

I was named to be a different man.

I was named to never forget the blessings I have.

REFLECTION

Reading and writing has always been my favorite form of expression, but I think it's easy to forget how important it can be to some of us when we grow used to writing intensive research and academic papers. While it is certainly important to grow composition and analytical skills (among other things), it can be debilitating to step back from expressing yourself and feeling like you're constantly working instead.

That has not been an issue I've had to struggle with over the semester. Participating in freewriting exercises through my ES 107: Chican@/Latin@ Lives class has truly been a cathartic experience, to say the least. On top of that, I've also been able to look back at some of those creative thoughts and further develop both their meaning and my writing. It's been an opportunity to reflect on some of my thoughts and transfer them from my mind, heart and soul onto paper.

A Journey to a New Life

Stephanie Brito

I remember the story as if it was told yesterday. It was summer, we were sitting outside in our backyard listening to old Spanish music. The fresh air was hitting our faces, the sun was setting, and the sky was clear and blue. After the sun went down the only light source we had was the shining moon and the stars. My sister asked my parents to tell us the story of how they came to the United States. My father was the first to tell his story. He said he came to the United States for the first time when he was eighteen, but that wasn't the time he came to stay. My parents' and my sister's journey to stay in the United States didn't start until 1990. They overcame many obstacles to achieve to their main goal: the American Dream.

My dad came to the United States by himself in July of 1990 in order to have a stable job and a home ready for my mom and sister after their arrival later that year. My father's brothers had told him to go up North to find better job opportunities, better paying jobs. He flew in from México, Distrito Federal to Tijuana where one of his brothers was waiting for him at the airport. He was left at a nearby hotel where one of his cousins was supposed to pick him up.

His cousin was a coyote and smuggled people into the United States for a living. This time, however, he did not bother to show up and instead sent someone else to pick my father up from the hotel. They took a taxi to the border. The taxi driver told them to get out of the car as quick as possible and run to the gated area because if they stood there it would be easier to get caught. A woman picked them up. She guided them and they walked from midnight until six in the morning in order to reach their destination: San Diego.

They later got to a house and stayed there from Sunday to Wednesday evening. My dad, along with three other people, got picked up and were taken to the train station. They were to take a train from from San Diego to San Juan Capistrano. After going through so many obstacles, he reached Santa Ana, where he was going to get picked up by one of his brothers who lived nearby. He said it took him at least one month to find a stable job in order to earn enough money to pay for both my mom's and sister's arrival. It was 10 p.m. when my father finished his story. All we could hear was his silence.

My mother began telling her story. Her journey continued four months after my father's story left off. My mom and sister flew out of México D.F. to Tijuana in the morning. The same uncle who picked my dad up picked both my mom and sister up at the airport. They got to Tijuana and my uncle took them both to eat breakfast. After they finished they went on their way to find the man who was going to help them cross the border. He said they couldn't cross that day because there were a lot of people patrolling the border so instead they went to go buy blankets. That same night, the man took both of them to a hotel to spend the night in order to wake up early and be ready to cross.

He returned the next day to pick them up and left them at the house of the coyote. This coyote helped them across and left them in a McDonald's. At the restaurant they met with the person who was going to take them to meet my dad and uncle. Finally, they were reunited as a family, together, trying to achieve the "American Dream" they had all worked so hard for. After my mom told her story the silence was interrupted by her sobbing. My mom's sobbing and the crickets.

The Difficulty of My Name

Iridian Casárez

My name is Iridian* not Iridian. It's pronounced in Spanish not in English.

"What does your name mean?"
"Isn't it an element?"
"Where is it from?"

My name has no meaning. It's just a name. No the element you're thinking of is Iridium. My parents are from Mexico, so it's from Mexico? Well, here's where they found my name:

My mom and dad were sitting on the couch watching television. They were watching one of those Sabado Gigante shows where they seek out new talent, or something of that sort, and a contestant named Iridian went on to perform, she was a singer. The name caught my parents attention and they loved it so much they decided to name me Iridian.

I love my name.

One thing that I don't like about my name is the fact that it's a name most people haven't seen before so they don't know how to pronounce it.

Iridian is what my parents named me, but because some people can't pronounce it, most of the time I go by Iridian.

It began when my mother was signing me up for school. She gave the paperwork with my full name and when the receptionist asked how to pronounce my name, my mother said, "Iridian". After countless attempts of trying to pronounce my name correctly, the receptionist came up with the English pronunciation of my name. Since then I have been Iridian.

From kindergarten all the way through my second year of college I have been Iridian. To friends, coworkers, classmates, teachers, staff members, and employers my name is Iridian. It's a lot simpler to introduce myself as Iridian than Iridian. It's easier than going through the ten minutes it'll take for them to actually get it right before they then forget how to pronounce it within five minutes.

It wasn't until a few months ago that I realized that I changed the pronunciation of my name for the convenience of others. So now, I want to honor my parents' decision to name me Iridian.
I try to introduce myself as Iridian a lot more now but people still can't pronounce it.

So far the only person who isn't in my family that pronounces my name correctly is my Chican@/Latin@ Lives professor.
(Iridian* is italicized and bolded to emphasize its pronunciation in Spanish.)

The Mom Who Sleeps In the Car

Stephanie Castro-Hernández

María Guadalupe Hernández is a single mother of twins. She was blessed with a son and daughter. She is a strong woman and works hard. She is resilient, encouraging, and a smart mother who never needed a man to help her.

María Guadalupe, is my beautiful mom. She is my everything, mi todo. I would shake heaven and earth for her. She's been through a lot and continues to refuse defeat. Never did she miss any of my piano recitals nor Steve's football games, even after having to work without rest. She never received any form of government subsidies. We never got a step dad. She stopped being a woman for us. Never did she say she was tired. Never did she depend on anyone or ask for help. She did everything on her own.

Even when she was tired, she was there. Working from five in the afternoon to two in the morning Monday through Friday was not easy. She was always on-time picking us up from school, personalizing our lunches with a note, "Te Amo," followed by a self-portrait. She really never had time to sleep. The only time she was able to sleep was Saturday morning while we were in catechism class. My mom always kept us occupied, therefore she was always occupied. She attended every school event, parent meetings, and booster clubs. You name it; my mom was there.

She was the mom who sleeps in the car. Students always asked, "Why is your mom always sleeping in the car? Why is she alone?" I simply answered, "Because she's mom and dad." Truthfully, growing up I saw my situation was better than my peers' who had both a mom and a dad in their household. I'm so thankful everyday que Dios me dió mi mami, una gran mujer y madre. The mom who sleeps in the car is my mom, and she still never rests.

REFLECTION

I have always had a passion to write. I have the stories and the voice, but not the English skills. In this class, I was able to ignore the writing standards of a white male-dominated culture's English language rules. English, is not my first language so that is why I stall when I write. Even after taking a remedial English class in college, I just chose to freewrite without having to feel bad about my English.

In class we were all able to write and share our stories. Grammar in this class did not hold me back. It was great that I wrote and was inspired by the great authors we read in class. Their Spanglish writing is what I like to write. Spanglish gives my writing a more sentimental feeling. I'm proud of my writing, and I got such great feedback. It's unbelievable how our story will be heard by a larger audience. Most importantly, we were encouraged to just write! I did not write "fancy" stories but they are my stories and my family's, unique and different from the rest.

I loved learning and writing in this class. It was a truly amazing experience.

Ser Xingona

Graciela Chipres

La mujer buena no habla recio, ni dice malas palabras.
La mujer buena es delicada y no le gusta ensuciarse.
La mujer buena tiene pelo largo y siempre se maquilla.
La mujer buena es pura, abnegada,
y no tiene deseos carnales.

Yo no soy, ni quisiera ser, una mujer buena.
¿Porqué ser buena cuando puedo ser xingona?

¡Y yo soy xingona!

Me gusta expresarme sin pelos en la lengua.
Me gusta carcajearme en voz alta y sin miedo.
Me gusta ser fuerte y no me da miedo ensuciarme.
Me arreglo cómo y cuándo yo quiera.

Me corto todo el pelo para darme libertad.
Me deleito en mis imperfecciones y
en las pasiones de mi corazón y cuerpo.
Ser xingona es amor propio.

Ámense.

I Say

Michelle Cuevas

They say we can't even speak Spanish correctly.

They say we are dark as mud.

They say we are short, that is how we are distinguished from other Mexicans.

They say we are poor.

They look down on us.

They say that we are ugly.

They say we are fat.

They say we are so stuck in our culture and question why we don't move on--forward.

They say we are useless.

They say we just come to the U.S. to take from the government.

They say we dress "funny."

BUT...

I say we are just here looking for that "Sueño Americano" just like the rest of our raza and people from all over the world who have come looking for the same thing.

I say we are rich because we keep our culture strong.

I say our faldas y nuestros rebosos are hermosos and colorful like the arcoiris.

I say we know the difference between being happy and wanting more money.

I say nuestro dialecto is a code that gives us a powerful voice, one that can't be found anywhere else.

I say mi raza is beautiful.

A Lie

Gabriela De La Torre

My dad calls, "¿Cómo te va, mi chula?"

I lie. "Bien papá, todo bien."

"¿Hay algo que no te pareció? ¿Quieres que vaya por tí?"

"No papá, gracias." I fake laughter.

The truth is — I'm not telling him the truth.
        I'm not really okay.
                I am not telling him everything.

I'm not telling him
that everyday I feel like I don't belong.
I don't tell him
about the looks me and my friends get on the bus.

I don't tell him
about the men in their trucks,
revving their engines,
as I hurry on the crosswalk.

I will never tell him about the man at the bus stop.

Never.

I was not hurt, but I felt so unsafe,
like
I am not ready for the real world.

My dad has always told me,
"Gabby, no sabes lo que hay allá 'fuera."

Rebellious I replied,
"Well, I will never know--if you don't let me (go out there)."

Well, he let me,

and

I don't feel as brave as I used to feel.
I am not as fearless as I used to be.

I bought pepper spray.

I look over my shoulder constantly.

I don't feel safe.

Fluid in Different Worlds

Emjay Díaz

As a queer first generation Chicanx college student, I have faced many obstacles throughout my life. I have had to manage between worlds: the American world through the English view; transition to the Spanish world—proud of being Mexican; and a Queer world—where I was always being judged. The worlds' I navigate through, up to this day keep alienating me. Not two worlds, but three worlds--in one colonized globe. People keep judging and oppressing other people based on their identities.

As a child, I was told by my father that I was no one in this world, just another nobody in society. According to him, I had the "wrong" friends, made the "wrong" decisions, and "wrong" actions became what I did. I rarely had anyone pushing me forward to succeed. Teachers tried to encourage me to engage more with my education; however, at the end of the day my home always shaped my point of view in the world.

Change and a long process has brought me to where I am now. Everything seemed to go from wrong to wrong, making it right. One afternoon I was walking the streets of downtown LA with a friend. Suddenly, a green vehicle pulled us over, one of the passengers pulled out a handgun and pointed it straight at me. They were looking for someone. My mind went blank; that someone was me. A loud scream from the guy holding the gun, Plah! The gun went off. All I heard was laughter coming from inside of the vehicle. My mind was still blank, while the anxiety was rapidly building-up inside of me. I could not have told my mother, never mind my father!

Somehow, my mother knew. She always found out, always without my father's help. She sent me away. I was only thirteen years old, surviving the challenges from living in a gang-affiliated neighborhood. At that moment, my identity and view of the world changed drastically. I lost half a year of school when I had to leave L.A. Eventually I returned, and I was a different. Life is change, a work in progress.

When I was fourteen, I had no choice but to confront my family. I was returning from a long day at school, keep in mind everyday at school is a long day; my family (cousins, siblings, aunts, uncles, my mom, and not my father) were just sitting there, staring at me — often I felt hostility at home, but this time it was suffocating. I had no choice, I mean the way I dressed already had given my relatives an idea.

They trapped and cornered me. They needed to judge me. I confronted them and spoke my truth. I got acceptance, rejection, and mixed feelings. Two months later, I chopped off my long beautiful thick hair. Chopping off my hair set me free from a floating cage of judgment. High school was another world, one that got me to where I am now. After four years, high school led me to the changes I have done in my young life up to now. Leaving home was the best thing I could have ever done for myself.

After such an experience, my views will still be in constant change. My self-love, self-acceptance, self motivation are still works in progress today. I choose to believe in myself beyond what I think I am capable of doing in this world. I choose to love myself, and feel comfortable with myself. Encouraged by having succeeded beyond my early dreams, I stay optimistic for myself and for the future ahead of me. If I do not take leadership and control over my life, then where will end up?

Nameless

Emjay Díaz

Everything changed the day I decided to cut my hair short. Transitioning from middle school to high school was difficult. I got the stares from head to toe. Some students looked confused, others just went their separate ways. Students had no choice but to deal with me because we went to the same school. The routine of freshman year was: go to school and survive. The first couple of days of school were all about being alert, scared, and anxious in silent panics. I thought choosing which restroom to use would be my biggest concern, but the struggle involved all sports, the locker rooms, classmates, teachers, and unfortunately, family and friends as well. Ignorance frustrates me, but I also sympathize to a certain point. Many people who live in marginalized communities may not have the education and knowledge on certain topics. Not being open-minded, being exposed to only one point of view, may cause harm to people, to some intentionally and others unintentionally.

This is what happened. My biology teacher did not show up one day, so we had a substitute teacher. I disliked when we had subs in high school, especially during my freshman year. After my freshman year I got used to it. The sub was a lovely woman of color whose name I forgot, the experience though has stayed with me. I hated roll call. I didn't dislike my name but my appearance, my gender performance, made roll call an event. I did not hate my appearance. "Oh, damn! I do look very handsome when I get my fresh cuts!" HAHA. :) I hated roll call because I feared teachers would question my appearance because my gender performance did not match my name.

So we had this sub and she was calling roll and then got to my name: "María Diaz?" That day I did not see it coming, honestly. I raised my hand; she looked at me and looked at the roll call. I was chilling, trying to be cool, fuck man my blood was boiling slowly.

She said, "You are joking right? Guys, I have no time to be playing around." I showed her my notebook, somehow I thought it will validate who I was, but not even my classmates were able to convince her I was the person named María Diaz indeed. That exchange was only a sixty second conversation, after which I stormed out of class. My mood changed in a flash. It sucked having to deal with a daily exclusion from my life, at school and at home.

I walked and took deep breaths, drank some water and went back to class. Where else was I going to go? I had no one and nowhere to run to. That single event changed me, scarred me, yet also strengthened me. I know now, in college, that I may be singled-out and targeted because of my complex identities, but now that will not stop me. I will not be stopped by one name.

I am...

A Person of Color   Lower Class   Working Class
   Non-Binary   Transgender   Queer   Gay   Both   Woman   Man
Marginalized   Oppressed   Discriminated   Strong
   Determined   Powerful   Disgraced   Excluded   Included
Strong   Educated   Destructible   Unstoppable   Unbreakable

Lovable

I am me,

And no one can to tell me who I am and who I am not,
who I should be or should not be,
what to do or not do.

I do not have to validate myself to anyone,
not even you...

You be you and do you.

A House in México

Judith Domínguez

He lived the majority of his life in a pueblo that was poverty stricken, living on a day-to-day basis, working in the fields. How much does a campesino, a farm worker, make? A campesino's pay would be based on the amount of work completed per day, the wages are determined by the employer. After a hard day at work he would go home to his wife and children, they were his pride and joy. His children loved going to school and couldn't wait to go home to enjoy their mom's cooking and watch T.V. before bedtime.

Suddenly, the Mexican economy crashed and rash decisions were made. The children were between the ages of nine and twelve years old. The older ones had to drop-out of school before 4th grade to help around the house and to work. This man was never ashamed of his job. This man was my grandpa Alfonso.
Every day he would wake-up around 4 a.m. to start his day; my grandpa did his best to make sure there was food on the table. There were times when my father and his siblings would go to bed hungry or would share one box of cookies, among eight children, for dinner.

As the head of the family, my grandpa made sure his kids had their basic needs met, such as a roof over their heads and clothing, even if they were hand-me-downs. Because he worked as hard as he did, he made all of his children wise and taught them the value of working. This man was an inspiration to the people who interacted with him. Day and night he would work, and occasionally echarse unas cervezas after a long day.

Eventually, all of his children grew up and left their home. Some came to the States searching for opportunities. They made sure to take care of their parents by sending money to México whenever their parents needed it. Always happy in their little home, my grandpa lived to be ninety and my grandma died at eighty-nine. Orphaned, my father now is the family's inspiration to work hard. My parents taught us to live moral and wise in lives.

I am thankful to my grandparents and to my parents for giving us the best life they could especially when times were rough. Every day that passes by, I make sure to work just as hard as my parents did when they were growing up. I see a lot of my grandpa and grandma in my dad. Through him I still feel their presence. Just like my grandpa, my dad always taught my siblings and I the value of hard work and a good work ethic.

I met my grandparents for the first time was when I was about five or six years old. It feels like it was just yesterday, their house was full of life and I woke up to the smell of coffee at seven in the morning. My grandparents, sat on their chairs by the door and stared at the sky as if the clouds were telling them a story. They greeted us when they heard our laughter. How could I know, at that moment, that anything was going to happen to them? But something did. My grandparents' teachings were passed down and because of them our family is strong. Although my dad did not finish grade school, he continued to work hard.

I know my grandparents, from Heaven, look down at their son and smile, proud for his many achievements in being a good brother, father, and grandfather.

REFLECTION

Writing about personal information on paper as an assignment meant a lot to me because I do not usually talk about my family or about myself. I feel very private about talking about my family and myself because others do not need an explanation of who I am. Most of the freewrites I wrote about, at the beginning of the semester, were semi-personal and vague. I did not focus on a certain person and did not mention names or relationships to me.

Once I became more comfortable with the class and got to know the students better, I started to share information with them. All of the topics were interesting but the idea of writing in the moment was difficult because I have writer's anxiety and my mind does not flow. At times, against the instructions, I stopped "moving the pen" and drew on my freewrite instead.

For the topics that really did stand out, I talked about people I know and incorporated them without revealing their identity. Writing a freewrite on topics that related to me was actually awesome because I treated the freewrite as if they were my personal journal. It is not every day that I get asked questions about my family and about myself . At times, I actually planned on sharing personal information because in doing so I liberated myself.

Not everybody has the opportunity to hear my personal stories and I needed the courage to write or talk about them. Since family is such a sacred and private topic for me, I do not like sharing our stories with others. As a reader of the freewrites I chose to turn in, you can see which ones were really personal. I hope you enjoy reading them.

Growing Up In An Ill House

Suseth Fonseca

1.

I am her medicine
Until I fall exhausted in bed
I dream of peaceful conversations
Laughter being shared

But my reality is slightly different
It's a place where I cry and tense up
It hurts seeing my efforts not being appreciated
She says I waste too much time

But she does not know I do everything precisely
White rice quebradito
La carne jugosa y todo picado muy fino
I promise next time I will create the perfect plate for her

But nothing is perfect once those meds kick in
I suffer seeing her drugged up
She suffers when she is sober
For this reason, I believe we need help

But she believes I am useless
I rejoice when she says "Gracias por siempre estar ahí"
But then the medication kicks in and her joy is gone
I am a child of her illness.

2.

Physically, I became tired. Tired of multi tasking: from washing
dishes to running across the room to put Downey in the laundry. I
use my laziness as my resistance. I use it to resist her screams, and
the fights. When I hear her voice, my body quickly becomes numb,
and prepares to fight away her blows . People say I have become
her. Su gemela de carácter y físicamente. I have built a strong
attitude towards people, pushing them away just like she does to
people who love her. She does not realize that I learned that from
her, all she realizes is that I am rude to the people around us.

For those who stand on the outside of this bubble, it is easy for
them to give unrealistic advice. I remember laying in bed one day,
sick and tired: emotionally, mentally, and physically when my
aunt got there and started commenting on my laziness. She said,
"Mija, siempre estás dormida," but she does not realize I am
exhausted from not being appreciated for my hard work. Then,
my mom starts with her "Haces las cosas nomás porque las tienes
que hacer," because I do not put effort into the chores.

These chores have become hectic, from bathing her, to feeding her,
and cleaning the whole house. "No es fácil," le digo, but her
simple response is, "Véte a tu cuarto." She shuts me away thinking
it will teach me a lesson, but in reality it kills me even more. I have
developed depression from this entire situation, I cannot fake a
smile anymore. I have let my body become fat because I let her
throw me in the darkness. In the distance, I hear her cries every
night. She cries from pain, anxiety attacks, and being cold. It
irritates me when I hear my father tending her needs at two and
three in the morning, when he works at 5 a.m. My body chooses to
get sick as resistance, but my mind forces me to continue because
my father cannot do it all alone.

I miss my old self, the one before all her illnesses. The one who
had a small waist with fitted thighs, no stretch marks or lonjas.
Now, I am chubby with white stripes down my hips and inner
thighs. My family fat-shames me whenever they get an

opportunity, her illness is the cause of my overweight. How can I take care of myself when her health takes up all my time? She only worries about my physical appearance, but she should also be worrying for my mental health--before I go crazy.

I learned not to feel anymore because she criticizes every time I am depressed. "¡Ay Suseth! Otra vez con tus pendejadas, nomás en la calle estás feliz tú." However, when I am out with my friends, all my anger, stress, and depression go with me and I still walk around with a frown on my face.

3.

I used to just put my clothes away when she folded them. I would, or I used to, help her get things from the fridge because she could not bend over. We would make dad's bed together while she got ready. Mother and I would then clean the kitchen from top to bottom. We began from cabinet to cabinet, taking out all the expired cans. Then, we would make dinner for my father who would soon arrive, tired from work. I learned to make my special rice from my mother, the best cook in the world.

This all changed suddenly when my mother landed in the hospital due to a deadly infection in 2006. I remember staying over at my Tía Elena's house because my father and my Nina were with her. I would always ask my Tía how my mother was doing and she would only respond, "Well..." Her response was for a little girl and I was not a little girl anymore. Since then, I've had to say goodbye to my childhood and hello to motherhood.

My mother became physically impaired because the infection spread throughout her body, cutting off most of her circulation to her legs. She became dependent on a walker to move around, pero yo era su apoyo. At the age of ten, I became a mother figure to my sister. I had to take over my mother's role, no matter my age or my maturity level.

My chores became the kitchen, laundry, mopping, and her hygiene. My childhood life withered away without my consent. I learned to cook everything from fajitas to bistec ranchero con arroz rojo, bien cocinado. I cooked meals a ten year-old child should be eating, not cooking. I had to perfect each of her favorite dishes because otherwise she would not eat what I cooked. I learned how to cook some of her dishes, but she also had to adapt to my way of cooking. She analyzed the plate when it got to her table as if it were a life or death situation. "La cebolla no se pica asi, le falta sal, la carne está blanda o muy dorada, el pescado no me gusta tan aguado." Her complaints were a sharp knife cutting away at my dedication.

I had the dedication to exceed her perfectionistic expectations, but the wounds I incurred have not healed. I still mess-up preparing certain foods, like overcooking the meat, but she has slowly shaped me with her sharp knife. I will never achieve perfection in her eyes. As a result, ironically, I have fallen in love with cooking because she has taught me so many meals with her strong attitude. The only thing I was able to perfect was the love I have for the kitchen.

Once again, I am her gemela, mother loved the kitchen before her illness attacked her. When it was time for her therapy to walk around the house, my body would become numb. This happened because I always knew a lot of screaming was coming my way. I always made a mess when I cooked. She would come by the kitchen, and I am not exaggerating here, but her first step into the kitchen was a step coupled with a thousands complaints coming my way. "Esto no va aquí, que tiradero tienes, porqué no limpias antes de cocinar." I could never please her. My body, numb and stuck in the kitchen, realized her illness made her very cruel.

I remember the happy mother who used to lay in bed with us chanting, "¡Ahí viene el monstruo de la laguna verde!" and started tickling us until we fell off the bed. Then she would start singing, "Que Laureles Tan Verdes," just to annoy us. Then, my little sister Naty and I would leave her and go sleep because she had annoyed us already.

Now, I wish even her annoying self was back from the medication, because the current cruelty is affecting me. I miss my old mother. I wish I enjoyed her more before all this happened to her. Since my old mother is now drowning in medication, I have become her helper. Drowning her with 6 pills in the morning and 10 at night. The pills put her to sleep. Only then could I get chores done before she could wake up and order me to do them. I find a relief when she is asleep because she does not pressure me to clean her way. I give the chores proper attention to make them perfect for when she wakes up, and sees how nice the house looks. Then you will find me praying that she wakes up and notices the difference

4.

Nurses running back and forth, beating machines, blinding lights, and prayers whispered by my family. Un Padre Nuestro y un Ave María. It all started with el llanto that prohibited la válvula to close. I was diagnosed with a window in my aorta that leaked blood into my lungs. I lived in an ICU incubator for 18 days. A premature baby in a crystal glass bed where I was connected to multiple machines, keeping me alive. The two nurses, my guardian angels, were always watching over me.

Un Domingo, 21 de Septiembre del 1996 estaba en un cuarto oscuro donde yo estaba conectada a muchos aparatos para mantenerme viva. A priest, my parents, and my family arrived at the hospital where a cardiologist was waiting for them with life-changing news.

I was only two months old when my heart was surgically removed and placed in a machine where it would pump on its own. The machine pumped all this strength and courage into my heart to continue living. Fuí un milagro. Tengo que seguir viviendo porque Dios me dió otra oportunidad para seguir en este mundo. Me dió una oportunidad y fuerza para poder lidiar con cualquier obstáculo. Con la Virgen de Guadalupe a mi lado pude salir adelante.

The scar runs seven inches, starting from my collarbone and down. A scar that the world can see with clothing with the slightest cleavage. A scar that might make me appear fragile, but it is a constant reminder that I am stronger than I seem. Yo pude sobrevivir una operación peligrosa y yo puedo sobrevivir todo obstáculo que la vida me ponga al frente. La máquina que le dio fuerza a mi corazón, me dio fuerza a mí para sobrevivir y enfrentar los maltratos, y gritos de mi madre. Esos gritos y maltratos me pueden tumbar, pero yo me levanto y sigo adelante.

Everything I have gone through with my mother, has worked like the machine that pumped my heart. The screams, the unappreciation, everything has pumped strength into me for whatever challenge may come my way.

Trabajo Con el Cuerpo

Suseth Fonseca

Mi papá trabaja con el cuerpo. Su papá lo sacó de la escuela a los 10 años para trabajar en la cosecha. Being the third oldest, he made him work to bring in more money for the family. Cuando tenía un descanso y regresaba a la casa se quitaba las botas para descansar. Mi tía Elena cocinaba, mientras mi abuelita se iba al pueblo comprando el mandado. My grandpa was a bracero in the U.S. who came home every year to enjoy his family for 8 months and then headed back to the U.S. for another seven years. My father followed his father's footsteps and crossed the border when he was 17 years old.

En Tijuana cruzó la frontera en un carruaje fúnebre donde se acostó en compañía de seis otras personas. He came here to work on a better job, but ended up working in factories. His whole life has consisted of cosecha or factory work. Whether electronic, food, or chemical waste facilities, my father worked in them. Dad is a strong, loving worker who does anything for his family. He is a man, who after working for hours, sleeps less because his daughters and his wife take up his nights.

When I was growing up, he came home cansado to deal with our antojos and our complaints of our "ruined" or "boring days." But, he sat there and listened because, finally, he is home with his girls. His girls, however, did not show much appreciation of his hard work at the time, but somehow made up for it in their playful summer vacations. During those vacations he encouraged us to keep up with our education "para que no acaben como yo . . . trabajando con el cuerpo porque no tengo educación." Now it's my turn to show him how much I appreciate his exhausting days after work. Cada vez que regreso al colegio su bendición me da las fuerzas para seguirle echando ganas para poder, un día, darle descanso a mi papá que ha trabajado mucho para darnos una buena vida.

REFLECTION

Writing is a freedom from all the memories inside me. I am able to bring those memories to life, setting them free from that dark room called my brain. These freewrites were my favorite part of the class because we all had similar but different stories to tell. My favorite prompt was the one telling a story that changed your life because prior to that moment I never knew how that story helped me change. After I finished my freewrite, I felt proud of myself because of the story I wrote.

The best part was being able to share [my writing] and get complements on the way I write. Sharing these freewrites helped me change and open up to people, I am a really introverted person but I was able to step out of my comfort zone and share my stories.

The process of writing these freewrites was straightforward. It was so easy to write something every day because even though I had not written in a long time, writing was once my passion. I did feel challenged because there were other amazing writers in that class who also helped me to grow as a writer. I did have trouble choosing only three freewrites to submit for publication because I had a lot of good ones. I did not think that some of my freewrites were appropriate for publishing, however. Overall, I enjoyed writing and having the opportunity to publish, which is so exciting.

Gracias.

Keeping Quiet

Brittany Gautier

In the backseat like a prison cell
where i refuse to yell for help,
where private undesired intercourse
is pressured by strong arms of explicit force

i hear suggestions from a male friend,
"should have taken self defense"

imagine his sweaty, shivering body
behind the dollar theater parking lot
i assume i'm cheap, dingy, ungodly
mantra of misplaced afterthoughts

i feel the need to apologize out of fear,
"next time, i promise to be clearer"

this experience would not be the last time
still building this awareness of mine
maybe i should have broadened my shoulders
maybe i should have been a heart much colder

from a lecture in health class freshman year
i couldn't remember to scream, "fire"

only four months past the first lesson
i ask to keep my dress on
but i'm drunk, feeble, unresisting
he doesn't know to stop insisting

societal acceptance of sinful genetic disposition
"boys will be boys"

unprotected and unsolicited
he was never taught how to listen
he fooled me once, and fooled me twice
responses to my claim cold as ice

suddenly in touch with the devil's silent flesh
we're victims turned rape apologists

four months later and a new lover
he may not treat me like the others
but he looks at me with accusing eyes
foreign force, my displeasure, all lies

thinking i'm looking for pity, he asks me
"why are you telling me these things?"

after keeping trauma quiet for two years,
searching for survivors deemed legitimate,
i hesitantly open up to my little sister,
and she sweetly lets me in on a secret

"in the war against girls and women,
sharing these stories."

Something Sacrilegious For Your Unsatisfying Abuse

Brittany Gautier

how does one elicit this difficult wisdom?
"this act is not one of affection, but of pain"
being borne of mama's futile martyrdom
we all hope we'll all be saints

and when his serpent tongue turns your skin blue
and his love's rotten proof is poisoned fruit
why do we refuse to leave this mess undone
where there's no fair battle to be won?

mother mary, raped by the spirit
modern women hear this secret,

"i'm sorry father for i have sinned
by my throat he has me pinned"

as you patiently await his presents of peace
the regretful blessed pray for your release.

Mi Cultura y Yo

Daniel Gómez

The culture and traditions of México spread out all over the world. Those who live within a Mexican household will realize this in a few ways; whether they have their mom blasting Spanish music very early in the morning, or being able to smell all the amazing aromas of their mother's cooking. One tradition that a Mexican family could also do is enrolling their son or daughter in a folklórico dance group to learn the many regional dances of México. Growing up within a Mexican household, I was accustomed to these traditions except for being put into a folklórico group, which was what I had always wanted to do.

My interest in wanting to dance ballet folklórico Mexicano started when I was 10 years old. I attended a summer festival and noticed one of my friends was one of the folklórico dancers who would be dancing at the festival. I noticed her partner was wearing a charro suit. It was at that very moment that I wanted to learn how to dance folklórico. I had asked my parents if they could enroll me in folklórico classes, but they never did. I kept asking them to enroll me in folklórico classes for the next eight years, but they still didn't enroll me into any classes. Finally, I had an opportunity to dance folklórico at my high school.

In high school, I was a member of the tennis team. The head coach of the tennis team was also the director of the ballet folklorico group in my high school. He had asked me one day if I wanted to join the group and I would able to get out of conditioning with the tennis team. As much as I wanted to take that opportunity, I declined the offer because I was the team captain and I did not want the other tennis players to think that I the coach's favorite just because I decided to dance folklórico. I had to play the role of a team captain and the captain never leaves his group behind.

Finally after graduating from high school, I thought to myself, well I wasn't able to take folklórico classes thus far, but I was going to be attending Humboldt State University (HSU). Coming up to HSU, I wasn't sure if I was going to like it or not, because I was a student coming from the city of Norwalk, a city within Los Angeles County, and I would be living so far away from my family.

At the beginning of my freshmen year in 2013, I immediately started feeling homesick and cried every night. Around the third week of my freshmen year I was wondering what clubs and organizations Humboldt State University had to offer. I thought to myself, "I highly doubt there will be a ballet folklórico group up here, especially since Humboldt was predominantly a white community and the Hispanic population was around 15% at the time." At that point, I gave in to the realization that I would never be able to dance ballet folklórico Mexicano until I returned home in the summer or until I graduated from Humboldt State University. I did not know it yet, however, but my life would change that same week.

I was was already into my third week as a freshman. It was a Tuesday and I had just finished one of my classes and was headed back to the dorms so that I could rest until my last class of the day. As I was walking towards the UC Quad, I heard the familiar sound of mariachi music. It was a son Jalisciense. I started doing some footwork to the music. I saw two female students with long skirts tabling for their club. The two students noticed me dancing and ran to me and dragged me to their table, I found out that the club they were tabling for was for the Ballet Folklórico de Humboldt. My face had the biggest smile I have ever made because I finally found a folklórico group that I would be able to join. They told me that if I was interested in folklórico to join their group as well as enroll into the folklórico class offered by the Physical Education department.

I decided to join the group and after the first day of attending, I immediately fell in love with it. The professor Elizabeth Rivera and her daughter Leonora Rivera, who was also Elizabeth's assistant, were very impressed of how I was able to keep up for a

71

newcomer to the class who had no prior experience in folklórico other than watching dance groups performing at many different events. After eight long years of not being able to take classes, I was now part of a folklórico dance troupe at the collegiate level. If I had never found out about the Ballet Folklórico de Humboldt group, I most likely would have gone back to Norwalk to be closer to my family, but I'm very glad I found the folklórico group here and joined it.

By joining the Ballet Folklórico de Humboldt group at Humboldt State University, I got to meet many new friends, many of whom have danced folklórico since the age of eight. Other members were new to folklórico and, like myself, were just starting to learn how to dance. In the time I have been a member of the group, I have learned to dance around twenty-five to thirty different dances from different regions of México. I learned all the dances Elizabeth Rivera and her daughter Leonora were teaching us at an exceptionally fast pace and so I quickly became one of the most experienced dancers within the Ballet Folklórico de Humboldt.

Of the regions that I have learned dances from, such as Veracruz, el Norte, Sinaloa, Nayarit and Michoacán, my favorite is the regional dance of Jalisco. I enjoy it because it is the region that I have always seen represented at many festivals. I also enjoy the attire that is associated with these dances: the elegant traje con sombrero de charro. The women dance in colorful skirts with different patterns and colors. I also enjoy the music of the mariachi, as it is always lively and cheerful and full of excitement.

I had learned a lot during my first year dancing with the Ballet Folklórico de Humboldt. I got in better shape little by little. Despite being almost a 300-pound young man, I am trying to slim down. Just like when I am learning to dance a new regional dance, I know it takes time and commitment in order to achieve my goal. In February of this year, the Ballet Folklórico de Humboldt group attended the University Folklórico Summit, a three-day conference organized specifically for universities who have ballet folklórico groups in their institutions. During this conference, we learned about how to get our group out and known to the university, as well as how to fundraise for our group. We also got to connect with various university folklórico groups, like UC Santa Cruz, Fullerton, San Jose State, and UC Irvine.

With every dance I learn with the Ballet Folklórico de Humboldt, I gain more knowledge of the terminology of the dance steps as well as identifying when the music changes to start the next step in the dance. I have been dancing with the group for four years now. I have become a veteran dancer and the only guy in the group who has mastered every single dance our folklórico group has been taught.

With the dancing skills I have acquired in the four years I've been here, I have become a role model to some members in the group as well as an assistant in the class. Many faculty members from the university's Dance Department, the World Languages and Cultures Department and the Critical Race, Gender & Sexuality Studies Department have always complimented my dancing capabilities. During the folklórico class that is offered every semester at Humboldt State University, I am almost always in charge of teaching the men in the class the steps for each dance that we learn. I teach the students especially when we are learning a dance where the men are required to use machetes.

In dancing folklórico or any other type of dance style, I have learned that dance is not just an art, it also tells a story. The regional dances of México all tell a story from México's history. It is very important to keep the Mexican traditions and culture alive by telling these stories through the form of folklórico dance. By learning so many dances from the different regions of México, I plan on spreading and keeping Mexican culture alive at Humboldt State University for the remaining time I still have here by dancing with my folklórico group and in the future as well, when I become a folklórico dance instructor.

La Lucha

Una Guerrillera – A Woman Warrior

Estos son momentos que no quiero recordar, fuertes y dolorosos son parte de mi, los que me hacen la persona que soy hoy, no tengo palabras…

Recibí la llamada. Qué voy hacer?
No sé si puedo vivir así.
Mis hijos, qué va a ser de su futuro? Qué nos espera aquí?

Bueno. Ya!
Basta, no más!
Me voy al Norte, mis hijos también.
Esta vida no es para nosotros.

Esta es mi Lucha

Mis hermanos arreglaron que mis hijos se fueran con una tía.
Cansamos a los niños, que jugaran a llenar.
En la noche, bien cansados y bañados,
se fueron bajo la luz de la luna.
Nombres falsos.
Pasaron, sanos y salvos.
Las cosas eran más fáciles en esos tiempos.

Ahora, Mi Lucha!

Esta es mi Lucha como Madre.

A cruzar con el coyote por el cerro con una prima.
Mi corazón palpita en voz alta,
siento el latido de mi sangre en mis oídos,
a gatas, mis rodillas sienten las piedras,
el dolor es mi dolor, pero hay que seguir adelante,
Corriendo por mi vida,
corriendo por nuestro futuro como familia.
Saltando cercas, y cada una más cerca de mis hijos

Los voy a volver a ver.
Voy a sobrevivir.
Voy a vivir.

Con cuerpo cansado y mente fuerte seguí adelante.
Volteo a ver a mi prima, ya no puede.

Esta es Nuestra Lucha

Me mira, lágrimas corren sobre su piel, inmensamente cansada.
Me dice, "Perdón, pero ya no puedo, mi cuerpo ya no puede."
Su dolor y cansamiento dominan su cuerpo.
Que voy hacer? No la puedo dejar y no la puedo cargar.
Mi corazón quiere seguir adelante, pero en ese momento

Es Nuestra Lucha

Un señor nos mira y dijo,
"Ya mero llegamos!
No se den por vencidas!
Hemos venido de tan lejos… ya mero."

Saltamos por última vez.
Sus palabras fueron palabras de Dios.
Sin aliento ni esperanza, Dios lo mandó,
nos llenó de energía y fuerza.

Lo hicimos, llegamos a Los Ángeles.
Mi hermano nos recibió
para re-encontrarme con mis hijos
después de tanto tiempo y distancia.

Le llamé a mi esposo.
Ya llegué.

A empezar de nuevo.

Ahora Es Nuestra Lucha como Familia -- en el Norte.

Soy Una Mujer, Humana, Humilde, Fuerte, y Luchadora;
la que llamas "ilegal."

Beautiful Women

Sarah Guevara

They ask, "What are you?"
They will label me as an immigrant.
Until they don't hear an accent in my speech.
Until they find out I was born here.

Then, they will ask me, "Why is your skin so brown?"
I mention my mother.
They will label her as an immigrant.
Until they find out that she too has no accent,
And she was born here.

It is not until they ask about my grandmother,
that my eyes begin to water and my emotions, visible
like a glass window,
They know!

They will label her as an immigrant, an alien.
But I,

I will label her
a strong, brave, beautiful
Mexican woman.

That's who WE are.

Next Time

Sarah Guevara

Background Info: I lived with my grandma for about five or six years. Unfortunately, my mom was a single teen parent. My father passed away when I was only about one year old, the same day my mom was in labor with my younger sister. She was a 19-year-old single mom with no help from her partner. My mom was very depressed from my dad's passing. She turned to alcohol and drugs.

My grandmother was my caretaker for most of my childhood. Back then, I didn't understand why I couldn't see my mom, but I am grateful I didn't see her and she is also grateful that my grandma didn't let her see me. I love and appreciate my mom so much. She has gotten through a lot in her life and I am proud of the woman she is today.

I wake-up to the smell of cinnamon pancakes and the loud sounds from the T.V. It's 6:30 a.m. I look over at my cousins sleeping on the couch, and then at my aunts sleeping in the dining room on their bed. There were beds everywhere in that house. I lived in a two-bedroom house, my grandma's house. Twelve to fifteen people lived in it at any one time. Sunday mornings are what I remember most, eating breakfast on the couch and watching my favorite childhood show, "Lazy Town."

I was having too much fun with all my cousins to notice that my mom and dad were not around. I always remembered when my mom did come and visit. That day, my grandma suddenly came running from the kitchen and turned off the T.V, told me and my sisters and everyone else who lived there, "Shh! Be Quiet!" I wondered why. My big cousin said to me, "Your mom is here."

The moment I heard the word mom I got excited and start shouting, "Where? Where?" My grandma got my attention and shut me up quick. It was then that I heard a knock at the door and then my mom's voice. Everything went dead silent, only the loud pounding was heard. Nobody answered the door. I didn't know why. I hadn't seen my mom in a month or so. I wanted to yell out "Mom, come inside, I miss you!" but I couldn't, I didn't because my grandma was giving me the deadliest glare, and it scared the crap out of me. Soon, I could no longer hear my mom's voice and the pounding was gone. "I won't see my mom today," I thought. I'll wait for her. Until next time.

REFLECTION

Ever since kindergarten I have had trouble with my grammar and forming sentences. I'm not bilingual so that couldn't be the reason why I was "below average" in my grammar skills. It wasn't until my senior year of high school that I got an A+ on an essay I wrote. I was very proud of myself. I learned a lot from Mrs. Fischer, my senior English teacher, she was helpful. She had me meet with her and she helped me with my grammar instead of just putting an "F" on my essay.

One thing I learned from her English class that I didn't learn in any of the other English classes I had taken before is that in order to write your first draft it's okay to not know everything you need. First drafts are like practicing for the final draft--the one that matters. I would always put everything I got into my first draft and Mrs. Fischer told me that that's not what it's all about.

Coming into this Ethnic Studies class, I didn't know what to expect. I had taken a different Ethnic Studies class with the same instructor before and I honestly loved it. It was always a mystery what we were going to learn in class in addition to our reading assignments. I was shocked by the new information we learned, but I loved it and I am grateful I had the chance to take that class. I wanted to learn more so that is one reason I enrolled in Ethnic Studies 107 Chican@/Latin@ Lives class this semester. Like I said before, my grammar was not great at all, so coming into this class which required students to freewrite daily and provided the opportunity to share with others in the class, I was a nervous wreck. I didn't feel confident about my writings at all.

I have written, seen and read the progress I made throughout the twelve weeks of writing. After re-reading my freewrites I thought, "Wow! I wrote that!" It amazes me that I can write something so powerful. Especially because it is hard for me to express my emotions and feelings using only words. I have learned that it is a big stress reliever for me to write things out like this.

The prompts of the freewrites were relevant to my life experience and I found myself easily writing out everything. For a nineteen year-old woman, I've been through a lot. Most of the things I've been through have not been discussed with anybody. Writing on paper I feel like I was talking with someone, possibly to myself, but it helped me 100%. I am very grateful for this class. I think every student needs to take a class like this, one based on freewrites, uncensored, and powerful writings.

Race and Me

Mia Haro

I am privileged to be half white in America and that part of my "ethnic" half is Asian because, I am relatively accepted in today's society. I am privileged that my Korean side is light-skinned. My life would be completely different if I looked more Mexican than Korean and I am the same percentage of both. But I don't "look Mexican," or should I say, I don't look like what people assume Mexican people look like.

My life would be different if my Korean side was dark-skinned. I am privileged because the ethnic side that people do see is Asian, which is the "good" kind of ethnic to be in America. Even better, I am East Asian, which is thought to be better than Southern Asian, because of our lighter skin tone. Being Asian has "positive stereotypes"--if that is even possible. Smart, good at math, high achiever. I'm actually terrible at math.

Asians are seen as the "good ethnicity" because, I think, they have most successfully assimilated to American culture. They are hard workers who have made enough money to be accepted into the middle class that is typically white. But this doesn't compare to the stereotypes attached to Mexican people: lazy, criminals, and rapists.

These could have been the stereotypes of me if I looked more Mexican. These are the kinds of stereotypes that ruin lives and limit opportunities in life. Things shouldn't be this way, but they are, and we all have to do our best despite the stereotypes. We have to prove those stereotypes wrong every single day. I am privileged to look the way I do, but I can only imagine what my life would be like if I didn't.

REFLECTION

I really enjoyed the daily freewrites during class. I used to be pretty good at writing when I was younger but then I stopped during middle school. I think the freewrites have helped me begin writing again, which is really exciting for me. I am a perfectionist so if I am afraid that something isn't going to turn out well, I don't even want to start it. I think this expectation has something to do with why I hadn't taken up writing again until this class. I didn't want to start writing again because I didn't know what to write about and I didn't think what I wrote would be good enough. This class has helped me with both of those issues.

I am grateful for the thoughtful prompts because I don't think I would have come up with those ideas on my own. The prompts got me writing about things I don't think I would have written about otherwise. I didn't like everything I wrote during this class but at least it got me writing. This class has helped me realize that I'm not a terrible writer and that I just need to practice. Writing in class felt like writing in a journal, where I was able to write whatever I wanted without the fear of it being read if I didn't want it to be. I even wrote about some things that I've only told a few people in my life about and it felt good to get those thoughts down on paper, somehow it felt more real after writing it down.

Freewrites were a great opportunity for me to put words to all the ideas I have in my head and I'm sure I will continue to write more often after this class. I'm sure I am not the only one who feels this way in the class and I think the freewrites are a great opportunity for everyone to discover, or rediscover, that they can write.

True Strength

Michael Hernández Martínez

We all have a person in our life that we believe encompasses the true strength of a strong-willed human. That man, with an incredible willpower to overlook his physical, psychological, and biological needs for the sake of his family is Miguel Hernandez. As I grew-up and got wiser, I began to realize what I had failed to see at a young age: true strength is the will to prosper through adversity even if that means forsaking one's own happiness.

When I would go to work with this man, I would see the diligence and his meticulous force at play. When he would work, he would not leave the job until he was 100% satisfied with his work. He is fond and proud of every job he does because he gives it his all every day. The way he regenerates his body and spirit with such an amazing speed every night and get ready for the next morning astounds me. I am only nineteen years old and I find it extremely hard to do myself. His job is in construction. He puts his life at risk for the sake of bringing bread and butter to the dinner table at home. While he was coming home tired from a day's work all I did was sit around and watch television.

This man is my hero, my role model, and my will to not give up. When he bestowed   his few words of knowledge on me--all of which were said in a state of intoxication--I was too naïve to realize he had spoken through pain, wisdom, and experience. I never understood his use of alcohol, but I knew it gave him an ability to pour out his struggles. This man--who when sober seemed impenetrable--is a broken-hearted, injured, and shattered man. The alcohol allowed him to be weak for the night, at that time he would not feel ashamed of exposing his agony. He was too stubborn to admit he needed a friend or someone to listen to him. My mom detested seeing him drunk and would disregard him for the night. Drinking at nights, however, that was the only way he knew how to vent his pain.

One night which will forever be ingrained in my heart and my memory. He was drunk but playful, he showed his love to me by play-fighting. He always called me his "chaparro" but it wasn't until now that I realized how much hearing him call me that name really means to me. It gave me so much orgullo because that's the nickname he gave me. I always wanted a nickname, but I hadn't realized that I always had one. This night was the night when my perception of him changed from a drunk man to one of a strong-willed and powerful man. He was completely covered with dirt from head to toe, wearing his job's company shirt, raggedy black jeans, and shoes.

He was drunk. I was in my room and he called me to the living room. I saw him and instantly got frustrated because I hated talking to him while he was drunk. He sat me down next to him and immediately he started crying. This was the first time I saw my dad cry, tears running down his cheeks as he balled up his fist tight with frustration. He was crying, he said he was tired, that he, "Was done doing this."

I didn't know how to respond. I asked myself, "Had my dad been this miserable for so long?" He looked directly into my eyes, with tears still running down his face, and asked me to look at his hands. I looked and my heart broke into pieces. By the time I was done examining them, my heart was completely shattered. His hands were bruised, torn, and full of scars. His work was torturing his hands but he never had said anything. He was breaking his back, brutalizing his hands, and tormenting his head to pull his family out of poverty.

All that time all I was doing was going to school and doing my homework. Despite my efforts, I felt inept because I couldn't help him from decaying at his work. From that moment forward I put more effort into my own work and made a promise to myself that I would not let all his pain be taken for granted. That night I started the process of becoming a man. Though I did not know it at the time, he had been sacrificing his life for mine--and he still does. I am the proud son of Miguel Hernandez. I will work hard and become successful no matter how great the challenges will be. I will make my father proud.

Just our Secret?

Abraham Jiménez

My brother, Jonathan Jimenez, was diagnosed with Asperger Syndrome around the age of eight.

It is a form of Autism, a developmental disorder affecting the ability to socialize and communicate effectively. All I remember was that we had the same classes until the time he was diagnosed. He was transferred to another elementary school because mine did not offer classes for kids with conditions like his. I persistently asked my parents why he had to leave. They didn't tell me anything at first, but I always suspected something was off and different with him; he didn't talk like me, he didn't walk like me and he didn't go to the same classrooms I did. Because I was persistent, they told me when I turned ten. They told me he had Asperger and that he had to stay in Special Ed. classes until he showed signs that he could be in regular classes.
"Pero, no se lo digas a Johnny. No quiero que piense que ser diferente es malo o es raro."

"Okay, okay ma. Yo no voy a decir nada," and I didn't. I kept that secret from him for so long. I never told him when he and I were separated in elementary school and that he had to go to special classes with kids "just like him." I never told him when our parents pushed him more to read the extra page or take another hour to study for the upcoming test. I never told him when he was crying and asked me, "Why can't I be normal like you?" as if I were normal. I wanted to tell him, so that he could understand it, confront it, and deal with it.

I was, however, convinced it was beneficial for us both if he didn't know; he would continue with his life without knowing and I wouldn't feel bad. Because he didn't know what was happening, he hustled, harder than anyone I've ever known. All throughout middle school, he was still in Special Ed. classes and took a lot of abuse from people. By his junior year in high school, he earned his way into regular classes, and wouldn't you know it, he even had a couple with me. A couple of weeks before our graduation, I decided to tell him. If people were to ask, he would know and he could explain it in the way that only he could. So, I told him and he looked a bit shook. In the end, he nodded and said thank you. I thought he was going to flip or give me some sort of lecture about how I couldn't say anything before. Instead, he said, "I've always known that I was different.

But now it has a name: "Johnny's Gene."

REFLECTION

I registered to take this class around April or so of last semester. I didn't know what this class was going to be about except for the study of Chicano history and that seemed like a good class to take. I never considered myself Chicano, just another average white guy who had parents from Mexico. When I explained it to my parents, they seemed happy of the fact that I would get the opportunity to understand and know what the history of their people was. So, I went into it with some high hopes and expectations.

Right from the get-go, I was hooked. I felt proud to be a part of this Chicano culture. The professor explained to us that the word "Chicano" was used as an insult to people with a Mexican background several decades ago, but people started to take the word back and used it as a power move/symbol. If we were to call you "Chicana", you'd say "Hell yeah, I am!" That type of enthusiasm really is unparalleled when it comes to what you believe in and what you stand for.

I left the class the first day with orgullo y con las ganas para venir otra vez, and it became fun for the majority of the time being there. With the freewrites, we had a chance to connect with our classmates because many of us shared similar upbringings. It was nice to hear that this person had the same thing growing up as this person or that their parents made them the same dish growing up in the exact same way.

I Raise My Voice: A Reflection

Idette G. López Franco, Associate Editor

I was a student in the class that collectively conceived this journal and I am one of the authors in Volume 1. Later I became a Teaching Assistant for the same class and now I am one of the Associate Editors for Volume 2. I have had multiple vantage points from which I have engaged with CouRaGeouS Cuentos: A Journal of Counternarratives, and it is from this unique position that I write now.

CouRaGeouS Cuentos is a collection of the student's voices heard through our own poems and stories. We decided to share our stories with the world because we knew our voices are valuable and they matter. The ES 107 class focuses on the history of and literature by Chican@/Latin@s. This class created an opportunity for the students to make connections with our Chican@/Latin@ culture. Furthermore, it created a space where we could reflect on our own individual identity and position in the social hierarchy as a whole.

A few of the main themes we focused on were race, gender, sexuality, patriarchy, class, colonialism, oppression, and resistance. Our resistance to our erasure within academia is manifested in the sharing of our stories. As a student of ES 107, I learned about the Chican@/Latin@ history and its relevance to the people we are today. We should have learned the things we learned in ES 107 in elementary school. Sadly our history and our literature are hidden from us to cover up the white supremacist oppression of People of Color in the United States.

After every lecture I left knowing something new. I learned about the colonization of Mexico, the Treaty of Guadalupe Hidalgo, the social construction of the border, the racist political fiction of "illegal aliens" in the interest of U.S. capitalism, the separation of families through multiple moments of mass "repatriation," "removal" or "deportations," and of the introduction of religion that degraded my people's traditions and culture. These things I learned them all in my Chican@/ Latin@ Lives class.

The class not only created a community but also helped every student understand the history of Chican@/Latin@ Lives and the sociohistorical issues that frame what our community is about. It was a class where we learned about the Chican@/Latin@ history through works of literature by Chican@/Latin@ authors, we critiqued them and ultimately re-claimed them as our own.

As a whole, the experiences and needs of People of Color are definitively neglected or ignored throughout dominant social U.S. discourses. This dynamic is not different within the community of Humboldt State University (HSU). Many students come to HSU because of the natural environment, the great outdoors and to escape the stress and struggles from larger cities. The problem is that the campus is characterized through the University's marketing department, as a comfortable, welcoming, and accepting community. What they don't know or don't publicize are the underlying institutional structures that place People of Color at a disadvantage.

Most Latinx students who choose to enroll in HSU do not realize the way we are used by the University to access funds that are not necessarily spent to improve the quality of education for "Hispanic" students. Latinx students are unaware that there are local and organized hate groups within the community surrounding the university. Many students do not know that their peers of Color are attacked and disrespected by white, typically male youth, because they, as students of Color, are not welcomed here.

Many students who identify as People of Color have a hard time identifying with our professors because they do not look like us or represents our communities. The list of incidents of neglect, erasure, and exclusion is long. Even when we articulate these issues to the university, HSU fails to acknowledge our experiences as serious problems that need to be talked about and addressed. I was lucky that I was able to experience ES 107 from two different perspectives. This experience not only allowed me the opportunity to shape my own identity, but it also allowed me the chance to aid my peers in their own journey through this educational system. This was truly a humbling experience.

As a student in ES 107 Chican@/Latin@ Lives, I found the class amazing. This class felt safe, and in way familiar. We (the students) got to read stories about people like us, people that went through experiences that we could relate to. The readings were rewarding but the experience of hearing each other's stories during class fostered a sense of community that became critical in my development as a student. I could connect with my peers after a couple of weeks, I was able to speak up for myself, to read critically, to participate genuinely, to ask the important questions, and to hear each other's voices.

When I was given the opportunity to become a TA, I became more involved in what the students learned or discussed in the course. I was able to read their freewrites, listen to their questions and concerns, and become a source of support and encouragement for students who were now going through the same experience I once did. When I introduced myself to the students, I told them that even though I was their TA I would like to meet them on the same (hierarchical) level in the attempt to find a common ground between us.

Being a TA to me meant so much more than just a course that I would gain academic credit for. I wanted to be accessible to other students like me; I believe that as individuals we are constantly learning from those around us. Our professor told us time and time again that if we ask the students to share what potentially can be a point of vulnerability, that it is only ethical to have the same expectation about ourselves.

As a TA, I was able to read the students' work and learn about them, their history, their personalities, and their aspirations. These students are very brave to be willing to share a part of themselves with others. After reading their stories, I felt empowered by their voices. Their stories were acknowledged and they are valuable. As a Person of Color (POC), we are constantly marginalized by the academic world. This course allowed the students to use their voices in ways that truly represents who they are. When it came down to selecting the freewrites to be published, it was terribly hard to choose just one from each student. Every student's writing was unique. In the end I made my choices guided by current situations, ideas, and so on.

Sharing our stories, in order to better understanding each other made my experience in ES 107--as a student, Teacher Assistant, and Associate Editor of CouRaGeouS Cuentos — a richer one for all of us and allowed me to create memories I will never forget.

Pues Yo Digo

Yanel Lázaro Cardozo

They say that my parents only came here to not pay taxes.

They say that they only came here to steal jobs.

He says that the only kind of people Mexico sends over here are violent and rapists.

They say that we only eat beans and tortillas
and that we have too many tías, tíos, primas, and primos.

I say that most undocumented immigrants pay more in federal income taxes than Donald Trump

I say that that my parents came here to start over and give themselves and their children a life that they couldn't have if they were still in Mexico

And, what jobs are we stealing?

The jobs no one wants.

I say that Mexico sends some of the most hardworking people.

People who work early and late night shifts, only for them to say, "Qué necesitas?"

And yes, we do have many tias, tios, primas and primos
but we never have to worry about spending holidays alone.

And, hell yes! We do eat beans and tortillas,
with a lot of salsa and extra cheese too.

REFLECTION

Throughout the semester I really enjoyed the freewrites we had in class. I remember writing about my day in a journal when I was growing up, but I stopped after a while because "I got busy" or I simply forgot. To be honest, it has been years since I've actually been able to write down my thoughts on paper and not just write for a grade or make sure that the format was correct, which is why I really enjoyed writing in the first place. What also made it enjoyable was getting different topics to write about during each freewrite. Sometimes the topics were something I didn't really think about much but I did had a lot to write about.

Another aspect that I enjoyed about the freewrites was being able to hear what others in my class had to say because I feel that it's really important to see how other people view things differently. Not only that, listening to each other's freewrites gave me the insight that although most of my classmates grew up in a Latino community or home, we all grew up differently while also sharing similar experiences.

Lastly, I would really like to thank my professor for giving not only me but also my classmates the chance to do these freewrites in class. I really value everyone's story that was able to share or that I was able to read because I feel that everyone's voice and our stories are important. Being able to do these freewrites really gave me an insight on what a writer looks like and it's not only someone on the front cover of a book but it's maybe the person sitting next to us who decided to write down their thoughts on a piece of paper and share them with the world.

My Name...

María Mariscal

My full name is María Guadalupe Mariscal Hernandez. I added my mom's last name because I like it more than my dad's last name. In elementary school, they used to call me "Lupita." Personally, I don't like my first name because it's so common. Yet, I just can't see my name being anything else. My grandma, my mom, and I--we all have the same name.

The reason I was named María is because my mom believes in God. I was born prematurely with a slim chance of surviving. My mom named me María because when they told her that I wasn't going to make it she named me María, like the Virgin Mary. My family believes that I am a miracle baby. I am very fortunate to be alive today and I am always grateful for each and every day. Like I said before, I cannot imagine my name being anything but María. In Humboldt, I hardly ever hear that name which makes me happy because back home I hear it all the time.

¡Con Mucho Orgullo! / With Pride!

Aileen Martinez

Mexican.

Latina.

Chicana.

Hispanic.

These are labels that may describe me. But my race? I wouldn't know how to answer that question; none of the categories I listed are a race. I didn't notice this until I was filling out job applications and had to be categorized as "other." Or in some cases, they would list a bunch of races and then just isolate a box marked "Hispanic/Latino."

It makes me uncomfortable when people tell me my race would be white because my skin color isn't what is understood to be "black." I love being Mexican and I love my culture. The thought of being labeled as something I'm not makes me mad. It makes me mad that so many people in society believe that my culture is something I should be ashamed of. It makes me mad when I notice the funny looks I get as I speak on the phone in Spanish to my mom. Me da coraje que hay tanta ignorancia en el mundo.

Soy Mexicana y

Latina y

Chicana.

¡Y lo digo con mucho orgullo!

October 31st, 2015

Emma McCallum-Spalaris

Sorrow and loss. Grief. Death seems more real now, more prominent, more relative to me. I have come to know how to grieve alone, how to cry without stopping in the middle of the night, to literally howl at the fucking moon; how dare it shine so brightly still. Realizing I am alone, learning to cope with it, feeling loneliness consume me, and being ok with it. Grief experienced so raw consumes me every day. Night is pin pricked with dreams about crying. I have changed, I have grown a shell, a scabby callous over those wounds. Grieving for friends lost, childhood lost, the loss of familiar and predictable, the loss of stability, and the loss of sanity.

In loss there is also gain. I have become more in tune with myself, my feelings, my desires; I live an absolute true version of me. No one is holding me back, not myself, not him, no one can because I am sharp and I am cut and I can cut back. I am learning and growing, from grief to anger to newness--a new home, new friends, a new awareness of myself, and that is enough. I must keep growing, because pain has taught me many lessons, and many lessons have not yet been discovered.

REFLECTION

I am extremely grateful for the opportunity to be a part of this class. It was a gift. The freewrites were like nothing I had ever experienced before, because we were asked to write on and explore such personal topics. In other courses, I have been asked to write whatever came to mind, but none of that writing ever pushed as deeply into myself as the writing for this class did. Some days it was extremely difficult to write, due to exhaustion or not wanting to open those doors to the darker stuff inside me during a school day. Occasionally, my freewrites were simple fluffy drabbles and grocery lists, but when it was a good day, it was a good day. Pieces I wrote for this class are more personal and emotional than I have ever written before and it was cathartic.

Being encouraged to explore writing styles and techniques, and just let myself use my most inner experiences as the basis for my writing was such a journey, and one I loved. As a science major, most of the writing I do during a semester is research reports, abstracts and data collections. It was so comfortable to know I could have a safe space to write for 15 minutes once or twice a week, and write from the soul, from my raw self. Towards the end of the semester I started to really use my freewrites as a mode of exploration of my own mental illnesses and struggles with depression and severe anxiety.

The freewrites helped me start writing more outside of class as well, even attempting poetry. Writing feels like second nature now, it feels like a natural way to process my emotions and sort myself out, and I have seen the benefits of continuing to write, or keep a journal. I am so grateful to have such an encouraging teacher regarding creative self-exploration through writing. The freewrites were incredibly important parts of my semester, and for that I am thankful.

Songbird

Marlene Medina

He is the son of my grandfather
the one who was left behind

Left in his homeland
with his mother who loves him
more than anyone in this world

She has always told him how proud she is
of the man
he has become.

He grew up valuing family, strength, and hard work.

He whistled with the songbirds on his way to work.
On his spare time he enjoyed laughing and singing
with his friends in the mariachi band.

During rough times he listened to words of wisdom
and welcomed the comfort of his mother.
He admired her devotion as a single mother.

He thinks about how the years are passing by so quickly,
afraid of the day that he has to choose the piece of tierra
where he will place the tombstone for his mother.

A lump forms in his throat.
Tombstones always cause his eyes to tear up,
but he never lets a tear fall, instead he swallows his sadness.
His amá taught him never to cry
over things that have not yet passed.

On the days the sun was high,
and the breeze was warm,

he wondered what kind of man his father was.

At times he thought his father is a coward
not a real man,
but other times he thought
about all the things they could have in common

He wonders if his father is dead or alive...
Little did Xavier know that his father, José,
wondered about his son in Mexico, too

José wonders what type of man his son grew up to be
All the while listening to the songbirds perched above his head.

REFLECTION

I haven't written like this for the longest time. The last time I wrote
for a class about real life situations or feelings was in high school.
Writing for this class took me back to my ninth grade English class
with Ms.Villavazo. In her class I felt like I had the freedom to
speak my mind and freewrite about how I felt about any subject. I
felt the same freedom in this class even though the writing
exercise and prompts were different. I really felt like my voice
mattered, whether I decided to speak or not speak in class. There
was this safe space created to share our lives, knowledge, and
opinions with one another. This space was beautiful and really
built community in our classroom.

The process of writing was difficult at times and other times
writing was really easy too. I had difficulty writing about some
prompts because I couldn't relate to that prompt. I realized that
the reason I couldn't relate to some prompts was because I had
some privileges that my fellow classmates didn't have. I never had
experiences with U.S immigration policies or faced big injustices. I
never had moments when I was criticized for the color of my skin.
I always blended into the background and was never really
discriminated against on account of my race.

Although it was difficult to relate to certain prompts, these prompts gave me an opportunity to think about the people who do relate to these prompts and how it affects their lives. It gave me an insight to a different view of life that I didn't have. The ones that were easy to write about were ones about my change of consciousness, my otherness, my culture, and how I felt about diversity.

These prompts also brought to light my own intersectionality and strengthened my love for my culture. Honestly, coming into this class I felt like I wasn't Chicana enough to even be in this class or be able to speak-up during class! Through the process of writing and talking with my classmates about our prompts and about the books we read I have really grown to see the breath of my culture. I now feel stronger about my identity as a Chicana.

Brothers

Irán Ortiz

One was an athlete and one was a misfit.
One dreamed of setting records and one dreamed of girls.
One was passionate about music and
the other passionate about writing.

And they were both undocumented.

They both got accepted to college,
the first in their families,
Never knowing the impact they left
for those of us who saw them grow up.

His music grew to be his passion,
his fingers never left the keyboard.
The other had a way with words,
capable of communicating with anyone.

They were both undocumented.

His show packed the concert hall,
his 8-year-old cousin was struck with stardom.
His first magazine issue was published,
and his 13-year-old cousin was struck by words.

They are brothers, sons of an undocumented Mexican mother

Their hard work means a lot to her
but also to those around them.
They are my cousins, my inspiration,
and I hope one day,
to be as passionate as they are.

Mi Gente

Alejandra Palafox

I am ….. confused I don't know
how to feel exactly.
I see around me
and everyone is devastated.
It worries me, shouldn't I
be feeling the same?
I see them, I hear
and listen to what they need
to say and that's
when it hits me, mi gente
MI GENTE feels
like a broken compass.

Even after
voting I feel small
I feel powerless.
Going to classes I see
some of my professors, whom I have
a lot of respect for, they don't talk
the same, you notice it while
they teach.

Some admitted that they too--feel powerless.
It infuriates them because
they are the ones we go to,
to seek answers from and
now when they say something
we don't feel as
empowered because they too,
are terrified for us.

The Importance of Knowing the Language

Alejandra Palafox

My educational journey has changed the way I understand my life and the perplexity of my oppressions. Through this journey my goal was to educate myself so I could learn the language that describes what I was going through. The language gays need to know in order to stay true to themselves, to their own persons, to who they are. The language that offers an analysis of their positionality in this world.

I needed the language to talk to my mother about who I am and most importantly to be able to stand up for myself whenever I find myself being oppressed. I wanted to learn the language so I can then grow, so I can then, explain more than just my experiences, but critically analyze why these experiences pushed me to understand the language heterosexuals didn't need to know. I recognize that internalized oppressions, such as homophobia, exist. I know about self-silencing so my family wouldn't get shamed on my account.

I had trouble understanding this language at first because the terminology was all very new and difficult to fully understand. It was far beyond my vocabulary. That frustrated me because I recognized it. The reason I pushed myself to understand this language was so I can go back home and explain it to my mother. Explain to her who I am and what experiences I have gone through and still continue to go through. I want to have a conversation with her about that topic we never brought up again; the topic of my, "coming out." I want to have the conversation and be able to do so with more depth. I want to ask so many questions, questions I never got the chance to ask. I also want her to ask me questions, the ones she is always curious about.

Every time I go back home I realize I have made progress on who I am, however, I re-experience some oppressions I thought I had overcome already. Going back home I realize that that oppression hasn't fully gone away. At home I was able to get my mother to think more critically about some of my experience of oppression. She didn't quite understand what I meant until she started watching this show called, Los Casos Cerrados. In this show this lady is a judge and she defends gay people from heterosexuals because heterosexuals are so stubborn and refuse to understand that queer people exist and will continue to. After watching this show, she then understood what I meant by coming back home and having to deal with some oppressions I thought I had already dealt with and resolved. In that moment, I saw that she understood now, that she could see it now; she was allowing herself to be open and see these oppressions in our community.

Getting an education is important for my self-improvement and growth because without education I would continue to be experiencing my life without actually understanding why it is that my experiences lead me to feeling this way. I feel like I need to police myself so I stop experiencing homophobia, and unwillingly conform to my gender roles. As for the language I needed to learn, I learned in English; now I need to translate it into Spanish because my mother only speaks Spanish. This is something I am currently working on. In class we were asked what meta narrative we connect to, what well-known story mirrors our own story? I have not found a meta narrative that describes my story.

Revisiting One of My Oppressions

Alejandra Palafox

I grew up up as a Christian Latina
Wondering about my internal religious oppression.
I asked myself, "Am I still a Christian for sinning the way I did?"
Did I betray my religion for embracing my sexuality?

I still pray, you know, but I wonder if he still listens.
I don't go to church anymore, but I still believe in him.
Is our relationship still the same?
I know it's not, because this time I'm honest with myself.

I went to church this past summer, I felt his presence.
But it wasn't the same, I felt like an outsider.
This burden I carry of meeting the Christian expectation
Doesn't allow me to be fully at peace.

When I hear your name I pretend I didn't.

Te quiero olvidar pero, ¿cómo?
Mi testimonio contigo es lo que me une a tí,
Y es lo que me da la fortaleza para entrar a tu casa.

I want to forget about you, but how?
My testimony joins me to you,
And it's what gives me the Strength to walk into your house.

Dreams

Maricela Palafox

Those dreams we are all trying to fulfill are for our parents, of course, also for ourselves, but it's more for them. It's the joy in their eyes that is going to be the most fulfilling thing when they see that you have made it, graduated and surpassed them in life. It's them saying, "Yo no pude porque mis padres no tenían dinero. Y ese no es tu caso, tú sí vas a poder." In other words, "You don't have a legit excuse for not going to school because money is not an issue and we are not making you work at an early age as my parents had me do."

Parents have this mind set when coming to the United States that if they work hard enough they could someday be able to own their own house. That's what really drives them to keep going in life. When life happens, however, as with having babies, sometimes they have to put their dreams on pause and put all their focus on their kids. My parents started saying when I was very young, "You have to go to school and do well. That's your only job!" They made sure they got all our school supplies we needed to start our new school year. That is how they started to get us thinking that education is the only way out that the path to a good life is through school.

Education is always a topic that is brought up during the holidays, "How are you doing in school? How are things?" and, "When are you going to be done?" I like when some family members know when to stop. We all have those nosy uncles and aunts that just like to point things out and give their opinions that sometimes just get us so mad. I have noticed that the people in my family who went to college seem to be more understanding of what it really means to attend college. They tend to be more off-your-back and let you enjoy your vacation instead of talking about school because they know that is the last topic anyone wants to talk about. I really like that they understand when to back-off. The ones that didn't really attend college have a more narrow understanding of how tough it can get. They just think college is more schooling, which it is, but it's also harder.

The dream I am in pursuit of is getting my college diploma. That dream is what I am truly working for. Sometimes I just want to throw in the towel and say, "I'm done with all this!" I've wanted to do this so many times already! The only thing that keeps me going is that I'm almost done, so I just have to keep pushing. One challenge of being a college student is that you are learning more about yourself and then you have to make a decision about your life or career. This process is not something that comes easily because it makes you doubt everything you have done and it also makes you rethink if this is something that is worth all this stress.

Who would have thought that school could drain you emotionally, mentally, and physically? Man! Why didn't anybody mention that this was going to happen? I know they said college was going to be hard, but the things I am talking about are hard at another level. We do these things to make our parents proud, and of course for us too. Don't get me wrong, sometimes I do question why am I still in school if being here doesn't make me happy. Most of the time I feel mad because of all the stuff that needs to be done. Of course things don't just magically get done by themselves, I wish they did sometimes! Sometimes it feels like a drag to come to school, but I realize that I just need to keep on pushing; I am almost there. The struggle is so real. Figuring yourself out along the way is too.

El Esfuerzo De Encontrar El Camino Correcto

Maricela Palafox

¿Cuál idioma debo usar cuando sé hablar los dos?

Speaking English has its benefits
Pero cuando en familia, not so much
You have to be able to Spanish it out

A veces no practicamos tanto el español
And we go back to speaking English
Like a second home of comfort

A veces uno se pregunta ¿what to speak?
¿Español o ingles?
It's like having to choose from uno del otro

Pero a veces los dos juntos se sienten bien
¿Qué es known as Spanglish?
Eso sí lo sé, porque es español e inglés

Being able to mesh them together is natural
I don't know how, but it flows through

A veces siento que es otro idioma
que puedo hablar con mi gente

Es como otra puerta que me gusta abrir
y está allí todo el tiempo que me lo permite

Spanglish es otra manera de poder
hablar.

Mi Familia

Michelle Palafox

In the family picture of my going away party one can see my crazy little sister throwing up peace signs. My older sister was standing awkwardly and my mom was making a kissy face like always. My dad was standing, semi-smiling, next to my brother-in-law. I stood behind them and I was photographed with a caught-off-guard face.

This picture represents how we're all different but we still stand together like a family should. Many people see us as a rich family. Many people think our family is perfect. Many people think our lives are normal. Many people see how different we are and are so quick to judge. But no one can see, by just looking at the picture, how much struggle we have actually gone through.

No one can see the strangers laughing whenever my sister had a seizure in public. No one will see how we couldn't go out as a family because of my sister's seizures and behavior. No one will see how my sister got admitted to a mental hospital because her teacher thought she was crazy when she was five years old. No one will see how my mom had to stop working because my sister's life was at risk. No one will understand how broken we were. No one will see how although things were tough, we were still happy to have each other. In the picture, we all stood together, just as we have through good and bad times, just as every familia would.

REFLECTION

Freewriting has opened many doors of creativity that I never thought I had. I was never able to just write about anything the way we did for our freewrites in class. Usually I could only write a paragraph or a little less than that. However, throughout ES 107 I was able to write up to two pages on any assigned topic. I have always wondered why I was never able to complete a creative writing piece and I still don't know the answer. I feel that now, having written strong and meaningful freewrites has motivated me to improve my writing skills.

The process, from the first freewrite to the last one, was amazing. I am glad that now I am able to write about any topic that is given to me. The process of learning how to let my feelings out and write about them is amazing, and I am proud I am now able to accomplish that. It was hard at first, I am a little close-minded. Having a professor that is very open-minded and supportive of her students helped out alot.

I was always ashamed of sharing and explaining my freewrites to my peers, but when I finally shared, I felt comfortable and welcomed. Having peers who respected my thoughts in my freewrites is another reason why I believe my freewrites kept improving throughout the class. I am glad we had to write during every class time. Writing together made the class bond and we got stronger. My peers and I related in many different ways and that made writing more important to me.

Para Mis Amigas

Jesse Pedraza

One of my most vivid memories from my childhood started during recess back at my old elementary school in Los Angeles. Figueroa Street School was located on the corner of Figueroa and 111th Street, right smack in the hood. It was the home of the Dolphins. I attended this school 3 years: kindergarten, 1st, and 2nd grade. Recess was my favorite for many reasons. It was much more than my need to be outdoors, outside of the suffocating classroom. If I could, this is what I would say to her now, "Ms. Simpson, this isn't quite working for me, this traditional pedagogy is crowding me, I'm uneasy learning this way, and I have a need to move around. I'm punished for being too talkative, too hyper, too busy with my hands." Expressing myself, saying what I felt at that age could have changed my experience in school, but only if someone would have actually listened to me. I wish children were given that type of agency and allowed to blossom.

Sigh. This is a lot. This is a lot to remember.

It was more than that. I loved recess because I got to be with girls. My girlfriends. Mis amigas. I had 3, black and brown girls with whom I spent my childhood. Morenas. Mis amigas. We'd run to the yard and grab the ropes from a bucket at the recess cabinet and rush to untangle the ropes. We quickly ran to save our space on the playground. We'd take turns. I'd hold onto the ropes first and then we'd alternate. Our friendship was as if we were the four directions. East, South, West, North. We'd create magic together. A joy that was pure, innocent and required nothing more than 30 mins, two ropes, and our ability to be agile, quick to use our limbs. This was the very first time I ever felt my femhood be understood and supported. They were girls and I was a "boy," yet they treated me no differently. I felt part of a family — a family who had my back.

109

I felt the stares as I jumped. I felt the toxic masculinity bleed out from the eyes of the boys in my grade. I could see their desire to jump too but I could also see the fear that held them down to the ground. A pair of those eyes came from my cousin, Fabiola. Fabi, morenita, gordita, con su camisa grande and the pans (sweatpants) she'd wear on a daily basis. Her lazy ponytail would slip from the tight grip my tia tried to impose as she quickly got her ready for school each morning. There she was, friendless on a bench staring at me as I jumped. She glared at me and at my girlfriends. I'd glance up sometimes to look at her looking at me. Her stare was full of envy; her stare was that of her father and her mother. She watched and made observations, and saved the data to be used, against me, later on.

At 2:55 p.m. I'd wait for her at the gate. We'd walk home together to her house. My mom got out of work at 5 p.m. everyday. I'd have to wait for her at my cousin's house for the longest two hours of my life. Fabi and I had a complex relationship. For a moment during the walk home, she was Fabi Fabi and she'd let her guard down and was silly with me. Our walk home did not require her to be who she "ought" to be. She was funny and would make me laugh. As soon as got closer to her house, I could feel her ease subside.

She turned on me as soon as we got home. We fought immediately over small things, she was always trying to take things away from me and I was fighting to get them back. (If you're brown, growing up with a lot of cousins, you know how this goes, the constant playing, real emotions of comparison, jealousy, and mischief all intertwined.

It was during one of those moments that we got into, maybe, one of the biggest fights of my seven-year-old life. She pushed me, yelled at me, releasing all the hatred for me she had stored up during her day at school. She pushed me onto the fence behind her house. I stood there resisting. I was extremely skinny and was wearing my school uniform. Dark blue shorts and a small white polo shirt with my spaghetti arms swimming out of the sleeves. I pushed back.

I knew this moment was much more than fighting over the ball. Fabi was homophobic. Fabi and I both knew a secret. A secret revealed every time we'd look at each other. She hated it. She was queer and she knew it. I knew it. I knew I was queer and she did not like that either. Her aggressive pushing evolved into a toxic storm above us, "Faggot, puto, marica." I could feel those words on my skin; they tried to break me. I felt the cloudy sky overwhelm me. I was tired. I was fed-up with this shit. I pushed back like I never had before; given her size it was very rare for me to muster the courage to fight back--but not on that day. "Get off of me you stupid bitch!" I yelled at her and I smacked her ponytail off. "STOP IT. STOP IT!" Her mom overheard us fighting from the kitchen window.

That day everything changed. My aunt, María, who was a lot like her daughter—butch, wearing loose-fitted "boyish" clothes—came out of the house. Angrily she yelled at me and told me she was going to call my mom. I stopped and went inside the house. I was uncomfortable and unsafe there. I felt the same most of the time around my family members. I waited for round two. I was ready. I was fed up. Fabi came inside, with her messed-up ponytail, and continued her attack, "Jesse nomás le gusta andar con niñas en la escuela. No tiene amigos. Solo amigas." Her proclamation was precise, as if she had spent a good chunk of time preparing for this moment and this speech.

I looked at her and then at my aunt, tears in my eyes. Fabi had out-ed me to maybe the most dangerous, homophobic, and closeted person in our family. We all knew what Fabi was trying to say. It was the huge pink elephant in the room. It was the truth everyone had tried to bury under the rug. I screamed, " We're all fucking queer Tia!! ALL of us".

My Tía María saw right through me, Fabi, and herself. She knew what was happening. I was a reminder of why she'd only fuck my Tío on special occasions. My mom was called soon after that, after the fight, there was nothing left. I zoned-out for the rest of that day and survived. As I write this story now, two decades later, my memory both fogs and unravels. I can somewhat remember what happened to me at home, a bit too ugly, and I choose not to write about it here. Without a doubt that day changed everything. I still remember the beating, the blood, and the tears.

In retrospect, I went through what I would now call a "queer/fem" genocide. A robbery of the sum total of my joy. I have survived emotional, physical, and mental warfare for many years after that. The fem is always fucked with. Fem is always undervalued. Strangers, partners, and family members always try to be beat the fem out of our bodies, our souls, our very lives.

My femhood has survived. My femhood is who I am. It is the brilliance behind my work and it is the core of my activism. It is my resilience; it is what connects me to my humanity, to earth, to my people, to myself and to all the magic in the world. It was what connected me to mis amigas en second grade. It is what connects me to the deepest joy I have ever felt. It will be never be destroyed regardless how much people try to rob me of it.

REFLECTION

I shared this piece with a few muxeres in my life before submitting this to the journal and the reactions were all different. Some of these muxeres are part of the abuse I experienced. These muxeres are my family. I've come a long way into my healing, as it is a process and I believe it is one without a final destination. I must live with what I've been through. But what gives me strength and courage is sharing my historia. Porque hay muchxs Jesses y muchas Fabis y Marías en mi comunidad. Complex relationships intertwined with harsh lived realities, ones caused by colonialism and all its ugly tentacles.

I feel it is important for me to share this cuento for many reasons, but mostly I want to be able to memorialize my pain and my blood, I do not want my pain to have been shed in vain. I hope my life's stories serve a purpose and help cultivate the conversations necessary for healing. I am very grateful for the encouragement and support I have received during my writing process.

Look at me now

Anita Ramírez

They told me I wasn't going to graduate
They told me I would never be able to go to a university
They told me I was focused on girls too much
They told me I'm too silly
They told me I'd never leave my city
They told me I need to focus on a successful career

I showed them I can graduate
I showed them my diploma
I showed them my acceptance letter to
Humboldt State University

If I am focused on girls too much,
then that's okay because I am well known
If I am too silly,
then that's okay because I know how to have a little fun
If I really never did leave my city, how come I've already seen the
sunrise on the other side of the world and travelled all around the
country?
If I need to focus on a successful career then
it will be one that makes me happy and that helps others out.

The truth is

People will doubt me
People will say negative things l throughout my life
I am going to prove those who doubt me and those who are
negative
wrong

I am great and no one will stop me.

REFLECTION

This poem is a reflection on a time when someone doubted me or told me who I am without knowing me nor my background. This reflection is perfect for me because I feel that not many people really know me for who I am, my background, and the reasons behind what I do. This piece also gave me a chance to really look back at my accomplishments and it helped my self-esteem.

Actually, this class as a whole really helped my self-esteem, my writing, and academic perspective. It was an honor to take this class and write about subjects like this and hear other students' writing about other subjects and understand their viewpoints and their mindsets. As a first year student at HSU, being able to write like this makes me look forward to see what I can accomplish during my college experience and beyond.

5:38 p.m.

Geneba Revuelta

My grandmother is only fifty-four years old. Many people think she is young, and one would think that since she's not that old, her thinking might be different or even slightly different than people who are older than she is.

She was born in a rancho near Aguililla Michoacan, México whose name I cannot recall. She now has five kids, four of them are married and my uncle still lives with her. He is about a year younger than I am and he is the result of my grandmother's adventures when she was single and going out to the bailes.

My uncle's name is Helder, he and I were raised the same, yet different gender expectations were forced on us. All my life I asked my grandmother, Why? Why is it ok that he never picks-up his own plate? Why was he the only one taught how drive, yet I, being the oldest, was not. Living with my grandma so that I might remain in the U.S. and hope to get a better education was raising a lot of questions for me. Why is he the only one able to go out with his friends at night? Why does he never even make his own meal or clean his room?

It wasn't fair. Her responses became less valid, less good enough, as I got older. "Porque él es el hombre de la casa," or "Porque te tienes que acostumbrar para cuando te cases." The preferential treatment towards him and the disregard of my existence, as a young and thriving woman, was always evident. I played sports, had a 4.0 GPA average, volunteered my time, and was involved with various clubs. My grandma would acknowledge that all I did was good--but it was expected from me because I'm a girl. If he did anything out of the ordinary, however, she would brag about it to her comadres. "¡Pues éste que trabajador me salió! ¡Ayer me cortó la yarda sin que yo le dijiera!"

5:37 p.m. the phone rings. I am now in college in my second semester and doing well academically. I receive a phone call from her. "You should come back you have responsibilities here too, remember, you're a woman and as a woman you are not fulfilling your duties."

5:39 p.m. Yes, I'm good. I really like it here at Humboldt State. It's great and I have a lot of friends. I was struggling with some schoolwork but I sought and received help and ended up doing okay. I am also playing lacrosse and my GPA is now a 3.7. It is not that great, but I'm trying.

5:38 p.m. The call was already over.

Beautiful Home and Family

Guadalupe Reynosa

When I was five years old, I lived in a beautiful home full of happiness and peace. No internet connection, barely a signal to watch TV and barely a signal to make a phone call. It was a home in which I felt healthy, free, and open minded, and especially, loved. I considered myself lucky until one day, when my father come home from work, and he was really excited that he had gotten a job offer in a different town, maybe a half-hour away. At that time, my home made me feel like I could be all myself and joyful, it was one where, by other people's standards, we didn't have much.

We shared beds. The "little" ones got to sleep with my parents, including myself. My oldest brother slept in the living room with barely any space. I still think that my father wanted us to move into a new house, a new community, because he wanted us to have other children to be social with, play sports, and get involved with our community. When we were living in our first home, we didn't go out much, nor did we associate with people on a daily basis. We lived in the middle of nowhere, 45 minutes away from town and from school; behind some mountains, in a little trailer.

On Sundays, my family went into town to grab groceries for the week, get some burgers and my two uncles who lived with us and who watched me grow up came along too. I remember my uncles helping my parents take care of me while they went into town or to work sometimes. These two super uncles, who I continue to love, are the uncles who chased after me when I didn't let them braid my hair. Sometimes I wonder what my life would be like, if we stayed where we were.

Now, that we live in Fortuna. I no longer live with my two uncles or see them every day. One of them lives with my aunt within a five-minute drive from our home. The other… he was deported and sent back to Mexico even though he was in the legal process of "getting his papers." My uncle is beautiful and genuine; he has a kind soul and is a father of two beautiful boys. My uncle, has been separated from his family, he no longer has the opportunity to parent his own children and teach them all that he knows. He will not be by their side while they grow up. His family spends half a year in the U.S. so his wife can work and save enough money to go to México and spend the other half of the year with him.

One of his sons has autism, but in my opinion he is the most intelligent one. My uncle's wife came to the United States back in 2009, pregnant with a beautiful baby girl who died in utero the week before her due date. She was forced to go through "a normal labor" without getting the chance to hear her baby cry. My uncle was not there for his wife nor was he given the opportunity to see nor hold his baby girl, the child he already loved so much.

Very few people truly know what the life of an "illegal immigrant" is like, what their families go through, and how much they are affected by federal anti-immigration policies.

I still drive by my old home. I do so because I love to replay the memories in my head. I re-create the images of the happy times with my family. I will never know what would've happened if we had stayed there. Would my uncle who got deported, still be with us or would I be where I am today. I now have the academic opportunity to learn about the history of my people and about People of Color. Today, I am thankful. I wish for the people who are oppressed the opportunity to be with their families, to be together forever. This writing piece is an unfinished story. I say this because the fight continues. I will not give up until I have my uncle back with us, the day I see him with his family and his autistic son.

REFLECTION

I have never really sat down to write. I have never thought to myself that writing is a great source of expressing yourself. I never really knew how many words you can actually write in fifteen minutes, without being distracted or uncomfortable of writing your own stories. Reflecting on the outcome of the freewrites during this semester, I have grown as a writer, but also more of a wiser individual. I thank our professor for giving us the space to write and for giving us the opportunity to learn more about ourselves. She has always said that our stories should not be judged, that they should be heard. We all have stories. Stories, that I believe we need to analyze and write about. You may end up like me and realize what you have gone through in your life. I have realized I have been both oppressed and resilient; that I have never stood up for myself.

These freewrites have helped me grow my self-esteem because I know that I am important and thus what I write is important as well. While writing my freewrite, "from a different point of view," I really didn't know where I was going with it during class time. After a while when I went back to look at them, it all made sense and I knew I had to continue writing. I know that we all have people in our lives that try to bring us down, but those people are people you don't need. The reality is that you should never have someone who brings negativity to your life affect your life's decisions. I wrote about this specific moment because it is one that I believe is important in my life. I also wrote about "Beautiful Home and Family."

A family is what makes a home and my family is the most important thing in my life, which is why I decided to write my story about them and what made my home so precious. I also wrote about what I know. "Yo sí sé--Yes I know." It is important to remind ourselves what we are capable of and consider ourselves valuable because of who we are and what we do. This Ethnic Studies course has truly opened my eyes to what writing is all about, and especially to what it takes to be a great writer.

Changes

Christian Rivera

School was over. The bell's ring signaled the freedom of youthful souls just like a gunshot signals the start of a race at a track meet. I sprint out of class, running so fast I can feel the wind caress my face and the classroom windows seem to pass by, almost as if I was soaring by the classes instead of running. But, by the time I reach the pickup zone my dad hadn't arrived yet. Isaiah, my best friend, challenged me to a game of rock paper scissors before he took off, and of course I won. I was left sitting on blue benches, gazing in awe at the blue skies above the school as the sun warmed the back of my neck.

The smells of fresh cut grass and unsmogged cars bombarded my nostrils while my attention turned from sky to where the sound of the paletero's bell could possibly be coming from. I can't see him but I know he'll come, he always does. Oddly enough though, instead of growing louder the bells begin to fade away. How strange, I really wanted a paleta de limón con chile. Oh well, there's always tomorrow. Off in the distance, I could hear the very distinct sound of my dad's car. That old car was more commotion than get up and go. Nevertheless, I'm glad he arrived. He approached me and I could tell something wasn't right. He was looking at me the same way he looked at me when he had to tell me he didn't have time to play catch--I knew something was up. His brakes screamed and his car came to a very slow stop right in front of me but I didn't want to get in. I took the biggest breath of my life and then got in the car.

"Mijo" he said, but I would not reply. Finally, the dreadful word "mijo" punched me in the stomach. "Today was your last day here at school. We're moving." Right away I screamed, "No dad I have to say bye to my friends!" I kicked, I screamed some more, I even tried to get out of the car. "Cálmate Chaparro, cálmate!" I started to cry. I wondered, "What is next? Where are we going? Are there any paleteros there?" I didn't want to move again.

Capella: Two Golden Stars

Gabriela Rivera Almansa

My favorite stories are ones about my grandfather. Born in 1916 in Cuba, Candido Almansa was one of the youngest of four siblings from a humble household. He was an orphan by the age of 8 and was taken in by his older brother who worked at the town's barbershop. My grandfather started working at a young age, helping out his brother in the shop and selling fruits around town. By the age of 16, he moved to the capital of Cuba and started working for a wealthy family as their gardener. The lady of the house became interested in teaching my grandfather manners and important life lessons like how to save money. It was this background that shaped him into the hard-working and committed man so many people knew and loved.

The family he worked for owned many factories in the city, and he started working as a tool and die maker. By the time Fidel Castro came around, my grandfather was a hard-working man who had no intention of letting anyone dictate what he could do with his business. My grandfather knew he had to get his family out from under that oppressive regime, so when the opportunity arose, he uprooted his life and moved to Long Island. There he worked 80 hours a week without a vacation, making parts for guns used during the Vietnam War. After 6 years of hard work and determination, he saved up enough money to move to Puerto Rico where the climate and sense of community were similar to Cuba's.

My grandfather sacrificed a lot for his family. With only a 6th grade education, he started a successful business. He instilled values of hard work and perseverance, and was a wonderful role model to my mother. Throughout their journey to the States, my mother was a young girl who did not speak English. She got bullied in school and felt embarrassed when speaking in front of others. This only fueled her resolve to become fully bilingual, and now she is an English professor who helps others learn the same language she had such a hard time learning. When I see my mother, I see my grandfather's strong work ethic and determination.

As a professor, my mother always includes a broader narrative in her classroom. She often teaches stories written by minorities who have been overlooked in most schools' curriculums. It was with her that I encountered my love for Alice Walker and Maya Angelou. My mother also nourishes wonderful relationships with her students. Oftentimes, when we are all out at the mall or the grocery store she bumps into one of her students. The joy in their faces at seeing my mother, even years after taking her class in some cases, is one I know comes from a true appreciation of her.

Both my grandfather and my mother are two clear examples of how your circumstances do not have to dictate your entire life. Their dedication and love for their crafts are what inspire me to go to school every day and work my hardest. I can only hope to one day make them both as proud of me as I am to come from a lineage of tremendously hardworking people.

REFLECTION

When asked to write about someone whose life of work and sacrifice for me has inspired me to work hard and achieve my goals, I immediately thought of my mother and of my grandfather. Of all the people in my life, these two people have been the ones to constantly support my plans and decisions. Even though my grandfather passed away when I was in 8th grade, I still remember so many of his teachings. He was the most hard-working man I'd ever met and he made sure to consistently provide for his family. I wanted to write something that included my mother as well, because she inherited all of my grandfather's hard-working characteristics.

My grandfather fought to make sure he had saved enough money and be able to leave it for his children. My mother currently works more than she ever has in order to make sure I am able finish my college education in the States. She sacrifices so much so that I can have a better life, which is exactly what her father did for her. I titled my freewrite "Capella: Two Golden Stars" after looking up constellations made up of only two stars. I found the title fitting because that was the theme of the prompt, my constellation. I think my constellation of support is much brighter than just two, but these two stars were/are the most important ones, the ones that shine the brightest.

Nuestros Sueños

Nancy L. Roman

I am the youngest of five children. Ever since I can remember education has always been important to my parents. I remember when my siblings were sick and they told my parents, thinking they would get to stay home. My parents told them, "As long as you can walk you can still go to school." I still apply this to my college life because it's what I learned.

I remember asking my parents a little bit about their migration to the United States and I remember them telling me that they both were very young, my mom was 15 and my dad was 14 years old. My parents didn't come to the U.S. together, as they didn't know each other then, but they met here. My mom was able to go to school until 8th grade and my dad was able to go up to la secundaria, better known as middle school. I also remember them telling me that they didn't get much education because they had to stop going to school so they could get a job in order to help their family financially.

My dad always tells me, "Ever since I could walk I started working." My parents weren't able to get as far in their education as they wished they had. So they always instilled the importance of education in us, it would be the one thing that would help us not worry about our future. They wanted us to have a career that would give us the benefits that they never had access to. For example, they want us to get a career that pays very well and that gives full benefits, whether it is dental and/or medical or both. They just wanted us to be set for life and not worry about struggling to make ends meet. They saw education as the first stepping stone to get to the career that would give us everything we need.

My siblings and I graduated from high school, but they all decided to work, go to school, or do both. Both my sisters stopped going to community college, my oldest brother kept working because he didn't want to continue his education, and my other brother went to community college on and off for about a year or two. Additionally, my oldest sister got married at such a young age and was a stay at home wife, but decided to go back to school to try and help her husband with the bills. My other sister only works because she couldn't figure out what she wanted to major in, which left work as her only choice. My brother, the second youngest in the family, has been on and off with school because he constantly switches his major to do things that pay well rather than what he wants to do; he also worked during this time and stopped going to school for a while because he liked the idea of having money in his pocket.

I believe that these circumstances are what lead to them being in the positions they are in. Watching my siblings struggle with their futures motivated me to pursue a higher education and attend a college because I knew it was up to me to be the one that made something of myself. I'm not saying that they didn't make anything of themselves I'm just trying to imply that they still struggle financially, so I knew I had to be different. Now, two of my oldest siblings just work, my other sister went back to community college and became a preschool teacher for a church, and my other brother is still going to school and working. I am the only one in my family who left to go to a four-year university that was far away from home.

School is very important not only to myself, but to my family; it means a better future for them and me. School also means knowledge; with knowledge comes wisdom and learning about yourself and others. I will be able to be a role model for my niece and nephews by becoming successful in school and my future career. I will be teaching my niece and nephews that you can't let your present define your current situation. School helps you choose what you want to do in life by exploring the different careers your college offers. It also helps you decide what you are and aren't interested in. Through higher education and a great career I will be able to help my family financially or make them proud of what I do and who I will become. Growing up I promised myself a couple of things in order to be different.

I promised myself to graduate high school with a GPA that would help me get into some great colleges. I worked hard throughout my high school career and did a lot of extracurricular activities. I then promised myself to work hard enough in high school to get into a four-year university and hopefully graduate in four years. My parents advised me to just go to school and only focus on that, so I decided to just be a full-time student at the moment, because I'd rather not have anything interfere with my studies.

I remember going to México, for the summer before my freshman year of college, and met my grandma for the first time. I remember pulling up in the cab in front of her small little shack. I remember my parents were talking with her and I started crying. My parents asked me why I was crying and I said it was because of my grandma's little shack. I know my grandma loves her little shack, but I realized that I take so much for granted. When I saw how small her home was and that it was built with anything they could find. I didn't know how she could live there or how she was comfortable in her home because of all the bugs, the dirt floor, no windows, etc.

I realized that it was due to her financial struggles in life that she couldn't afford to build a home like the ones in the U.S. I promised myself then that I would make my grandma's little shack a little better. I also promised myself that I would inspire my niece and nephews to become whoever they want to be and to always follow their dreams as cliché as that sounds. When they were born I helped my mom take care of them because my sisters and their husbands would work often. They became like my own kids. I try to achieve these promises by always following my heart/dreams and by stepping out of my comfort zone. It was hard leaving them when I came to college.

After meeting so many people on my trip to México, that are family or are considered family, they told me to try my hardest and to work hard. Some of them also told me that my family is counting on me to be successful. I am fulfilling their dreams of pursuing a higher education so that I can get a high paying job. Whenever I go home and my parents are talking to my family from México they hand me the phone so I can talk to them. The first thing they always ask me is how school is going. I say, "It's going well and it is very stressful." They then proceed to tell me a little bit about their life and how they wish they had been able to pursue higher education. They remind me they weren't able to because they had to help their family by getting a job when they were younger. After that they tell me to work hard and not give up. I know that I am not pursuing higher education just for me.

During high school I realized that I had lost most of my native language, Spanish. I promised myself then to try and take some classes to relearn my language and not forget who I was in the beginning. I took some courses in high school, which helped in that moment, but I still struggle with it, whether it is reading, writing, or the spoken word itself. I lost who I was due to not knowing Spanish well enough anymore. I still keep this promise to myself, which lead me to registering for a Spanish class in college that I will be taking next semester. I think relearning Spanish is so important to me because it is my way of feeling like I'm part of the Mexican culture.

I have assimilated so much that I don't know where the American side and Mexican side start or end. I think my education has contributed to me losing my Spanish because I was taught English at such young age that it made me forget most of my Spanish. Growing up I learned that in order for me to survive I would need to know English. This was ingrained in me because in order for me to fit in and be "American" I had to adapt.

In high school, I remember my teacher having us do a quick write about what our dream was; what we saw in our future. I remember writing about doing well in high school so I could attend a four-year university, which would lead to a sustainable lifestyle. However, coming to college and taking my *Ethnic Studies 480: Growing Up Chicana Latino* I realized that my dreams aren't necessarily mine. I am not only fulfilling my dreams, but the dreams of my family who never had the opportunity to finish their educational path. My family is relying on me to achieve this dream, only then will I be able to give back to them.

One of my goals in this dream that I have set for myself is to change and impact the world. I think that is why I love my major, Critical, Race, Gender, and Sexualitiy (CRGS), because this is what will help me take action in the world. The things I learn help me teach others, or at least listen to what I have to say. I don't know what I am going to do with my major, but I can't wait to see where it leads me. I promised myself to always learn and try new things. I try to keep this promise to myself by taking courses that I would find interesting or that I want to learn more about. I try to do outside research about these topics as well.

Sometimes it is a lot of pressure, because I feel like I can't enjoy other things since I am a full time student. From time to time I feel like I lose myself and forget why school is so important to me or why I am here, but then I remember that I am fulfilling not only my dreams, but the dreams of my family of achieving a better future, one that requires me to be financially stable. I am getting a college education not only for me; I am doing this for my family as well. I am succeeding for all of us.

Mi Viejo

Christian Sánchez

A_{pá}

When I was younger, my connection with you was weak.

Pensaba que estábamos conectados sólamente a través del fútbol.

I used to think that you saw me as a disappointment because of how you compared me to yourself when you were my age.

Ganadería y alimentación de los chivos temprano y cada día.

I slept till noon everyday.

Me llevabas a tu trabajo, "Para que aprendas cómo es trabajar sin educación."

While we have always had tremendous love for each other nuestra relación cambió después de nuestro viaje a México.

I was able to understand you and where you came from more deeply and emotionally.

He aprendido a apreciar lo que has hecho
y te quiero con todo mi ser.

You're a humble, simple, and hardworking man.

Somos padre e hijo como la vida es pasión y tiempo.

Dad

Algunas cosas que me recuerdan de usted

Dirt-filled fingernails, rough hard-working hands covered with scars;

Carne asada con pimiento de limón;

The smell of cologne after you take a shower;

La Selección Nacional Mexicana de Fútbol;

Fútbol en general;

Tuxcueca;

Vicente Fernández, La Arrolladora Banda El Limón, y cumbia;

Horses, bulls, and rodeos;

Un rancho Mexicano;

"Sí, pos sí." and, "No, pos no."

Albercas, como las que ayudas construir;

Pinto Lake Park where you would play soccer when we were younger;

Tu jardín atrás de la casa;

I see myself slowly turning into you

pero no es malo,

porque te quiero,

mi viejo.

REFLECTION

The first time I started a freewrite, I was confused because I was used to writing to specific prompts that looked for a specific, correct answer. These freewrites were very liberating because there was no correct answer to the prompts. I thought to myself that I was going to become fed up with all of these freewrites throughout the year. As time progressed, I really enjoyed writing them because I learned things about myself that I didn't know were there.

The first time, I was interested in poetry was when my oldest sister invited my family and I to watch a performance organized by a club that she was in. This multicultural club was called Rainbow Theater and students produced plays and presented poetry on issues pertaining to identity and society. I really enjoyed the poetry during these performances, but I never thought to write poetry of my own. When writing these freewrites, I used the knowledge I gained from these performances to help me write.

After doing more freewrites, writing came naturally to me. I had no trouble expressing how I felt about the prompts. The prompts helped me learn about myself and how the experiences in my life have shaped who I am today. Although, I didn't mind writing down my responses to the prompts, I had trouble volunteering to share with my classmates about what I had written. I did not share once during class any of my writing. Some days I would share the freewrites I had written with my older sister who was also in the class. Having her in that class was a relief, because without her, I wouldn't have wanted to enroll in the class. I learned many new things about her after she shared her freewrites in class.

Overall, this course has made me feel more connected to myself, my family, and my culture. I now understand the important experiences in my life and how they have helped shape who I am today. It also made me realize how important my family is and made me appreciate them as well as my culture as a whole.

Shit Gringos Have Said To Me

Marissa Lisette Sánchez

"Hey, soooooo like, what are you?"

"No, but like where are you reeeeally from?"

"Were you born here?"

"Where are your parents from?"

"I loooooove tacos!"

"Do you have a big family?"

"Ooooo! Muy caliente!"

"Mmmmm... spicy Latina!"

"It's just a joke!"

"Can you teach me curse words in Spanish?"

"You're not gonna start calling my papi, right?"

"Ayyy mamacita."

"Say something in Spanish!"

"Are you seriously using the race card right now?"

"Is your last name Hernandez? Rodriguez? Gonzales?"

"Holy moly, frijole!"

"Ughhh I wish I was as tan as you!"

"I love that you're so curvy!"

"You speak funny."

"I wish I had a Latina chick's body!"

"My girlfriend is Mexican too, I think you'd like her!"

"Do you speak Mexican?"

"She's Mexican too, I think you'd like her."

Dear white people,

Fucking stop.

My race isn't some kind of card I can play whenever I want to. This is my identity. It's not a tactic I play when I'm facing prejudice. Stop asking where I'm "really from." Mexican is not a language. Stop sexualizing my body. Stop fetishizing Latinx bodies. And for the love of God, don't you EVER, call me mamacita.

Sincerely,

A Brown Mujer who
        is sick-and-tired
                of your sexist and racist bullshit.

What They Don't Know

Marissa Lisette Sánchez

In a picture my abuelita is sitting at a table during what looks like a party. She is under a white tent and there are other tables and people in the background. My abuelita has a laptop in front of her.

When looking at this image others might assume that she is looking at a picture that is on a screen while attending a party.

Lo que no saben es lo especial que mi abuelita es para mí.

What people might not understand is that she was Skyping with me during her surprise birthday party that my family threw for her while I was at school. They don't know that this was the first time I wasn't with her to celebrate her birthday. They don't know that during that Skype session my entire family passed the laptop around because they all wanted to say hello. They do not know that my sister and cousin helped connect the call because no one else in my family knew how. They don't know that this gathering was the first time my entire family got together after my abuelito's passing in 2010, and I was not there.

No saben lo especial que mi abuelita es para mí.

People do not know that this moment was very significant to my life. They wouldn't know that after the video call ended, I cried in my dorm for 15 minutes. They don't know that this moment was the sole reason I wanted to drop out of college.

No saben lo especial que mi abuelita es para mí.

They don't know that she constantly asked me to go to a school closer to home. They don't know that leaving her to pursue my education was one of the most difficult things I have ever had to do. They don't know that every time, I find out that that she slipped in the bathroom, tripped in the kitchen, or has a bad fever I want to pack my bags and go back home to just hold her in my arms and never let go. They do not know that my abuelita is the heart string that keeps my family together--that scares me. Most importantly, just by looking at the picture, people will never understand just how much I love my abuelita.

Mi abuelita es muy especial para mí.

REFLECTION

Going into this class I wasn't expecting for it to be as healing as it was. I was having a really difficult semester.

I was struggling with my identity, trying to juggle school and work, trying to stay informed with current events but not allowing them to overwhelm me, and above all I was trying to be healthy, both physically and mentally. The emotions I experienced while reading the stories of people I could identify with were cathartic, almost religious. As soon as my pen touched that paper, for those daily freewrites, all my anxiety melted away. I had been in a funk for a while, one which caused me to stop writing altogether.

This class reminded me why I love writing and reading so much. Thank you to all of my peers in the class who were courageous and shared their stories. I know from experience that it is extremely difficult to surrender and become vulnerable, especially in front of people you don't really know. So thank you, thank you for sharing a part of yourselves with me. Our stories deserve to be heard. Our struggles and our successes deserve to be shouted out loud into the ether. I will fight beside you to make sure our voices are heard, because tu lucha es mi lucha.

No sé Porqué Nos Dejó

Jacqueline Santos

Oh no, my mom is upset and I can't figure out why. Daddy comes and then leaves every two years and I cry and cry and cry every single time. Matter fact, I throw myself on my bed and I throw all my toys all over the floor because I'm sad. My mom says she has had enough and tells daddy to either choose his family or to choose his job. Wow. He chose his job, and is now packing his things to leave. Daddy is leaving, daddy is leaving again. But why, why did he choose his job? Are we not important to him? I don't know why he is doing this. Only thing I do know is that his job is in México and we are in the U.S. I can't understand.

Is he leaving because I am not making him proud that I'm learning English in 2nd grade? Is it my and my little brother's fault that he is leaving because we follow mommy everywhere? Or is it because he is tired of picking me up from school on the bus because mommy had to take the car with her to work (little girl voice)? I am not sure if things are ever going to be the same or if I am ever going to see him again.

Mommy: Tu Papá se va a ir a México, ok?

Yo: Pero porqué Mami? Ya no me quiere?

Mommy: Él quiere estar sólo, todo va estar bien, te lo prometo.

Yo: Entonces él quiere tener otra familia en México?

Mommy: No se, pregúntale a él.

(Daddy walks into the room where things feel cold, where my little brother is sleeping)

Yo: Papi ya no me quieres?

Papi: No es eso, luego te veo mija, no se te olvide que te quiero mucho.

I cry and cry. Lloro y lloro.

Daddy shut the door. I feel like my heart is ripped out of my chest and stepped on all over the floor. He said goodbye without saying it…. My mom grabs me and says, "Vamos a estar bien, ya verás" as tears are coming down from her bright green eyes.

I am in college now. Until this day I have not heard from him, I don't know if he is alive or if he is dead. I do know he did not care about my family because, if he had, he would've never left my mom without any money struggling to pay rent that month. I'm hurt. I can't seem to get over this grudge. If given the opportunity, would I talk to him again after all these years? No, I don't believe so.

Expect the Unexpected

Gabriela Emelyn Torres

Third Grade ...

I am young, I do not pay attention to any negativity that is going on around me, I feel happy and there is no reason why I should not. My parents are happy together. Everyday I go to elementary school and back home. It is like being in paradise, everything is just right. I have no worries about anything.
I wake up, my mother is playing Banda, making breakfast for my father and all us kids. I see my siblings wake up one at a time, all excited for a new day. I see my parents hug and kiss. I hear a "Te amo," from my dad's deep voice as he heads out the door for a long day at work. He places a kiss on my forehead with the words, "Te miro al rato chaparrita." These are the ordinary moments of our everyday mornings.

I am lazy about going to school yet am also excited to be with all my third-grade friends. The day passes by. I spend my day playing in the playground, learning new vocabulary words, new math problems. The hours go by, getting closer and closer to the time when we can go home. Sitting on my chair, waiting for the bell to ring, I wonder how my sister is doing in her first-grade class. Finally, the bell rings, time to head on home, the home I long for. I can't wait for the late night soccer practice tonight. My mom and my dad take turns between my siblings and I and swing us holding our hands. We take pictures.

My siblings are too small to understand what was happening in the field, all they see are people running up and down. Everything is going well. We are constantly looking for my siblings, wondering where they have run off to now. My parents talk about the preparations of the carne asada we'll have this coming Sunday after my dad's game, as well as getting ready for the América vs Cruz Azul game. My mom is planning what to cook. Will it be pozole or maybe ceviche? Back on my parents' bed we are hit with a sudden wave of feeling tired, and one by one we start falling asleep. My mom's fingers stroke through my hair, I fight sleep, I do not want to leave the happiness of this day just yet. The last things I do feel are my dad's arms picking me up and placing me down on my bed, "buenas noches campeona."

Four years later …

It is a new day, we are living in a new house, in different city from four years ago, I am a seventh grader in a high school environment. Things have been tough lately, at home, at school, emotionally, mentally. I do not know my place right now.

I am an emotional wreck.

I am strong at home for my siblings but I do not know how to be strong for myself.

I am scared to go home now.

I am scared of anything that will start a fight, start an argument.

I am staying late at school today for softball tryouts, this is how I stay away.

I have homework to do.

I know some days are just great but I am constantly scared that today will be an off day.

I am tired of yelling, "Stop!"

I am tired of telling them to shut-up.

I am tired of trying to calm my siblings' tears because I cannot do so.

It has been a good week and the weekend is coming up. My dad's sister's birthday is just a couple of days away, and I am looking forward to meeting up with everyone in my family and continuing the happiness of this week, I hope this weekend will be pure happiness.

The weekend…

Today is Sunday, the last week of August, normally a great day. We are all getting ready, getting all the drinks we are taking to Pico Rivera, the food is already in the car. "Happy Birthday Tia Elvira," my sister says into my mom's phone. I am excited, all my cousins are going to be there, we are all expecting a sleepover and do the most we can during one of our rare get-togethers. I put the sodas into the trunk of our Chevrolet and suddenly I hear screams, my heart drops, I drop a box of sodas. I run back home, hoping I just heard the neighbors or something. I see my siblings crying by my parent's room. I am telling them to get into our room and stay in there. Here I go again, I try to stop the vocal war, I tell my parents to be quiet.

I tell them I am tired of living this way.

I tell them that enough is enough, to separate already.

My mom says, "Enough is enough," and she walks away. I get my siblings and tell them to get in the car quickly, I tell my mom to get in the car. I am disappointed in the way our Sunday is progressing. My dad is crazy, speaking words, making no sense; he repeats over and over again that we are not leaving. I fight, he tries to get the keys to our other car but I close the window. My mom continues to pull out of the driveway and I am crying. Why did it have to come to this…?

I shatter into a thousand pieces. I want to turn back and delete this day from our lives. My dad is not a bad person, having grow-up with him, I know that for a fact. He cares, he loves, he gives but what I can't understand today are his actions.

As I am writing this freewrite…

140

I am typing and looking back to these memories and see how none of us expected it, none of us saw it coming. I never expected the falling out of love. I still feel pain, but I see how things are way better now. My parents now can actually hold conversations and be at the same place with all of us. I do not see my mom with pain anymore. I see her happy, I see her better. I see my siblings better. I am better. I think my parents see their mistakes now.

I do not think they realized that by staying together for our sake it actually was hurting everyone more and more. I feel pain because my dad has not moved on, he still wishes he had done things differently, he admits his mistakes. I feel like that is why my parents have done so much better for us. They're friends with a past full of love, but parts of that past they do not like.

I wish they hadn't separated but I am glad everyone is better for it. I look back and can think of possibly better outcomes for my family but this outcome now is better than I expected. We are a family that does not see their parents together on a daily basis but we're a family who still lives connected, we have some boundaries rather than regret.

REFLECTION

How does one build the courage to write about moments one's life where everything felt so low, with no escape? Throughout every expected freewrite in the class I felt a pulling back telling me not to write about a specific event, to keep to myself and not let anyone know about the wrongs my family did or even ones I did. I worried about the judgment my peers might have about my life. What if the story I write does not express the impact it has on me. Freewrite after freewrite I felt a little sudden spark, the insight that overall I am writing these stories for myself. I relive moments in my life and analyze them in a whole different way. Most definitely I thought so much about the details I should include, what to say and what not to say, what I wanted to keep to myself and what I was okay with sharing. The biggest challenge to the process of writing my freewrites was wanting to write about someone I am not.

Each and every prompt had its own voice and I just wrote and wrote. One of the hardest parts was reliving the low parts of my life, coming to the realization that so many aspects of my life are not the same anymore and that is a good thing. Through the process, I was worried about not making anyone seem like a bad person because, in reality, no one included in my cuentos are, but their actions were. I remember sitting as I was revising my own story, I sat and sat and stared at my laptop, happy that I gathered the courage to write about things that have had a huge impact in my life, for the better.

I was an emotional wreck here and there, from a letter to my mom, a letter to my grandparents may they rest in peace, to the heartbreaking moment when my parents' separation was established in our lives. How do I let it all out without it coming back to haunt me?

I feel like I was scared to relive the moments through the writing process, but I see now that writing about them did me good. I see that things are better now, the relationship I have with my parents, the relationship that my parents have with each other, even after being separated. These freewrites have allowed me to open up to things I have wanted to open up for a while. They took time to write and plan accordingly but these freewrites came along just as life did, all I did was let my hand go freely, and my heart did the speaking.

I want to thank everyone involved in this process, for finally including a class where I felt comfortable letting my stories come out. I never felt judged. I can say that although I do not have a close relationship with everyone in our classroom, I felt like I could express anything and do so in any way I wanted to. Thank you for the creation of this amazing process, I am most grateful for being allowed to be a part of it, for giving me the opportunity to write my very own CouRaGeouS Cuento.

Carrying a Secret

Alejandra Valdez

When you carry a secret you sometimes have to lie to keep it. It was my 21st birthday, my whole family came to my house to celebrate, even my family from Arizona. It was one of the best birthdays I've had so far. One person was missing, however, my little sister. My aunt, uncle, and cousins all asked "Dónde está Carla?" My parents and I agreed to tell everyone the same thing "Oh, está con su amiga." My family in shock responded "How can she miss your birthday." I felt terrible for lying; I didn't want to make her look like the bad guy. What my family didn't know was that she was at the Children's Behavioral Health hospital.

I carried the secret inside me for half the day but finally spilled the beans to one of my closest cousins. I told her how it had been a tough couple of days and that my sister was showing signs of suicidal behavior. Since I live far away at school, I only heard about it when I got home and saw it for myself. My sister was making threats to kill herself and expressing how she hates everyone. I knew I had to get help for my sister so I called the police. I explained to my cousin how my parents didn't want anyone to know because we didn't want anyone to judge us.

There is a lot of stigma in our community regarding mental health, people don't think it's real or people are unaware of the resources available for help. As a Latina Psychology major the first thing family members ask me is "Vas a trabajar con locos?" I explain to my family how Psychology is about helping others, whether it is in mental health, advocacy, or research. I am glad I was able to be a resource for my family during this difficult moment. It was my 21st birthday and my little sister wasn't there.

The Truth Is

Alejandra Valdez

They say I'm too emotional.
They say I am a hopeless romantic.
They say I am self-centered because I am a Leo.
They say I am loud.
They say I'm too scared for change.
They say I will burn out quickly in my career.
They say people will forget me in a year.
They say I am "mixed" or Indian

The Truth is…

I am emotional because I care.
I am a hopeless romantic because I believe in the goodness of
people.
I am self-centered because I need to take care of myself.
I am loud because that's how we speak in my home.
I may be scared of change, but I did move 12 hours away from my
home.
Burnout does not stop me; I will figure it out.
Some may forget me, and many will remember me.
My skin color does not define who I am.
I am whoever I want to be.
I, and only I, am the author of my own story.

REFLECTION

When I found out we were going to do freewrites every class
period I was excited. Personally, I try my best to write in my
journal once a month. Being able to write whatever came to my
mind every Tuesday and Thursday was a game changer. In a way
I felt pressured, I kept wondering what other people were writing
about and whether I was answering the prompt correctly.
However, as the semester continued I didn't have to think much, I
was able to write the whole fifteen minutes non-stop. What

surprised me the most was writing about things I've never wrote about before. I guess these thoughts were just in the back of my head waiting to be written down despite the years that have passed. I would describe my writing style to be disorganized. I sometimes have so much to say and when I write I tend to jump between different topics or ideas. I'd rather have it all written down and then go back and organize my thoughts than worry about the flow first.

For a long time I found it easier to write down my thoughts than say them out loud to someone. When I write down what I am feeling or experiencing, I feel that there is no judgment or criticism, a feeling I like. I did, however, like that we had the option to share our freewrites with our classmates or just keep them to ourselves. The times I did share my freewrites it was liberating, sharing gave me courage and I appreciated the safe space in our classroom. Sometimes I was nervous sharing because I'd write about serious issues that I don't usually share with people.

Later in the semester, we turned in three of our best freewrites. At that moment, I realized we are all writers waiting for our story to be heard. I enjoyed reading other people's freewrites because each one was unique. The ones I turned in were mainly about my family and myself. One of them I was hesitant about mainly because I don't want my parents to ever read it. Sometimes you write things that can hurt people and I certainly do not want to do that to my parents. I still decided to turn it in because I felt it was important and had a big impact in my life. I'm still deciding whether I'm going to publish one of my freewrites and I kind of have an idea which one to choose.

Walking into our Chican@/Latin@ Lives class, I was prepared to learn more about our history and culture. What I didn't know was that I was going to feel like a true writer at the end of the semester. The class wasn't about grammar and proper writing but about writing with no limits nor restrictions. We read many greats books in class and now have an opportunity to be published, an opportunity many people do not have. I've enjoyed getting out of my comfort zone and learning what I am capable of achieving.

Esta, Es Para Mis Padres

Lucero Vargas Mendoza

Para mi Ami y mi Api.

El equipo más fuerte que existe.
Me han criado con Amor, Afecto y Paciencia
Atención, Apoyo, y Humildad
Son mi Luz, mi Fuerza, y más que nada, tienen mi corazón
completo
Con lágrimas de orgullo les escribo esta carta.

Han puesto todo su esfuerzo, energía, lágrimas, y amor en sus
hijos.
Nos han enseñado lo que es la Lucha,
Lucha de trabajo para seguir adelante.

Nos han enseñado Valor,
Valor de que no tengamos miedo a la vida,
de que nunca nos demos por vencidos.

Nos han enseñado Fe,
Fe en Dios, Fe en nosotros mismos, Fe que todo saldrá bien,
Fe que aunque estemos solos-ustedes siempre están con nosotros

Nos han enseñado Humildad,
Humildad, que no se nos olvide de dónde venimos,

Nos han enseñado lo que es una Familia,
a ayudarnos unos a los otros,
que si hay una tortilla, se comparte entre todos.

Nos han enseñado a ser Fuertes,
que nos demos nuestro propio valor y respeto.
Que la vida no es fácil, pero sí se puede.

GRACIAS!

Por su Apoyo en todo,
Apoyo escolar, Apoyo en nuestro sueños y
Apoyo hasta en mis locuras.

Por su Atención. Por estar en mis juegos cada fin de semana por
más de 10 años.
Por manejar más de dos horas para verme jugar y no poder
quedarse.
Por la Atención en llevarnos a campar, llevarnos de viaje, y
Atención de enseñarnos a ser fuertes, a que creciéramos gente de
corazón.

Por su Amor--el Amor en nuestras carcajadas, regañadas, risas,
lágrimas, y desacuerdos,
Amor en nuestros abrazos.

Por su Paciencia.
Cuando me dicen, "Haz lo que quieras!"
cuando bailan conmigo en medio de Mi Pueblo,
y cuando les digo de mis travesuras.

Por su Tiempo.
Siempre nos han puesto primero.

Por su Persona,
Por ser humanos increíbles, asombrosos, alegres, bailarines,
artistas, inteligentes, cantantes, y más que nada

Por ser MIS PADRES.

Por favor acuérdense y nunca se les olvide que son mi corazón
completo, mis number one, no le hace a dónde me lleve la vida.

No se sientan solos. Los traigo diario en mi mente y en mi corazón.

Y más que nada nunca se les olvide que son mi orgullo.

Love you

Su pedazo de carne y favorita,

la Cherro

Familia Vázquez

Kimberly Vázquez

In my family picture, I notice a whole lot of love. Others may notice a huge stereotypical Mexican family. Both observations are true. In the picture, you see my paternal grandfather, Grandpa Delfino, surrounded by all his children, grandchildren, and great-grandchildren. We are all smiling, some laughing, some of the little ones are moving around. My whole family is a mixture, half of us are light-skinned while the others are dark-skinned. We come from a long line of Indio Tarasco descent mixed in with people from Spain, hence the skin color difference. Although our skin color is different, we all have the same physical features.

Never once have we thought we were different from one another. My family originated in Tendeparacua, Michoacán. Our roots run deep there. We are proud of our mixed gene pool. We love hard, stick with one another, and never do we ever turn our backs on one another. This is strongly shown in the photograph. Yes, we're the typical huge Mexican family. We don't see ourselves as "different" because our family is our normal. Our normal is to be surrounded by lots of love, lots of laughter, and of course all our crazy selves.

We have a strong bloodline that won't die, same as our last name. The Vazquezes will be around for a long time due to the large number of males in my family. The males outnumber the females, three to one. Our last name will be passed down for generations to come. Every time I look at the photo, it makes me proud to say I'm a Vazquez. We are a hard loving, hard working, a big family, and I couldn't be more proud of that. We were all raised on a strong foundation of love. We fight like cats and dogs but at the end of the day all we have is each other. Blood is thicker than water, as they say.

REFLECTION

Throughout the semester of ES 107 Chican@/Latin@ Lives we wrote multiple freewrites, all with a different theme. We could make it our own, use different format, flow, writing etc. This work lead up to choosing three freewrites to edit and plan to submit to CouRaGeouS Cuentos. The freewrite I chose is titled "Familia Vázquez."

"Familia Vázquez" was written based on a family picture. I'm extremely close to everyone on my paternal side. We see each other daily and never turn our backs on each other. In all honesty, writing this made me miss everyone, unfortunately I couldn't see my whole family before I moved to Humboldt State. This freewrite was one of my favorites to write, it demonstrates the love in my family.

This semester helped me grow as a writer. I learned that I have a voice to be heard and I shouldn't be afraid to let it out. We all go through our own situations and many of us relate to one another in some form. No one in class was ever alone, there always was someone who had been through a similar experience. We are all connected. I've learned to never be ashamed of where I come from and about my life's story. The hardest moments in my life are pivotal events that have taught me the greatest of lessons.

Hand-Me-Down

Briana Yah-Díaz

To *mis palomitas,*

This is my third attempt at writing to you.

My first attempt was in class and my mental health was declining. What I wrote was a reflection of what I wanted to hear; I gave the advice I needed.

The second attempt was in the evening, two months later, my mental health was improving. I wrote about love. I noted the strengths each of you have and how I'm here for you both.

On this third attempt I write about survival. My mental health is balanced.

This institution isn't meant for people like us.

The media doesn't depict our people accurately.

Resist; take it over. #BlackLivesMatter. The education system caters to the white narrative.

Resist; don't give up and believe in your intelligence. They'll dismiss you *mijx por tu piel color de caramelo y mazapán.*

Resist; your existence *is* resistance. They'll impose their beauty standards on you *mijx porque no eres guerx.*

Resist; love yourself. They'll try to dictate *tus decisiones.*

Resist; your body—your choice.

They'll try to make you feel ashamed because *somos del barrio.* Resist; be proud of it. They'll feed you false ideas and try to mold you into who they want.

Resist. They'll try to silence you, **no te dejes.**

Resist; *maldito capitalismo,* don't consume what they produce.

Resist; *malditos roles de sexo,* don't allow them to define you.

Resist; *maldito racismo,* don't let them label you.

REVERSE RACISM ISN'T REAL.

Resist; *maldita institución,* never let them convince you broken glass is violence. Never let them convince you of *anything.*

War is violence.
> Homelessness is violence.
>> Racism is violence.
>>> Profit is violence.

Property can be replaced, your lives cannot. You matter.

I believe in you both.

No matter what they'll try to do don't forget how resilient you are. Don't put away the pain—feel it.

Mijx, you don't have to be modest in order to be respected... don't believe it.

You are more powerful than they say you are.
Be empowered *palomitas.*

I love both of you, unconditionally.

There's no predicting the future, only living through it and fighting.

Keep fighting *mis palomitas*.

Mijx, you don't belong in the U.S. Prison Industrial Complex...
don't believe it. You aren't what they say you are on the news.

Self-care is important.

You are enough. You are valued. You are needed. You are loved.

Take care of yourself first and never apologize for it.

You are water.
Powerful enough to drown,
soft enough to cleanse,
deep enough to save.

Remove toxic people from your life and do so without guilt.

Don't make room in your life for people who cause you pain or
make you feel small.

Let them go and hold yourself close.
Make yourself a priority.
Love yourself.

Call them out when they don't treat you the way you both deserve
to be treated.

Be full of life.

People, relationships, places, and material things will come and
go--it's part of being alive.

Choose yourselves over anything.

Use your voices.
Tell the truth with kindness.
We are all flawed, but flaws are not sins.
Support each other.

Your activism doesn't need proof to be real; it exists daily when your bones work against the morning's weight.

Stand with your people, not against them. If they watch passively as you struggle—they aren't your people.

You don't owe this society anything that it didn't already take away.

Acknowledge your privileges. Listen to the stories actively silenced by this society. Be an ally.

If you feel like giving up look in a mirror
       and embrace
              that your existence alone
                     is an act of resistance.

I am here for you both. *Creo en ustedes como ustedes creen en mí.*

Los quiero mucho,

Palomita

REFLECTION

This class is my safe space.

We all created this space; it has helped me survive the semester. I look forward to ES 107 every week. The people. The environment. The cuentos. The days my depression and anxiety start to war, this space offers me peace.

This space inspired me to create and write the piece I submitted. I wrote this piece to my babies — my niece and my nephew. I wrote my consejos to them with the hope my words will guide them through the structural, internal, and emotional highs and lows of their lives.

This piece is for anyone who needs these words.

Maria believes in me, in the power of my words, and in the importance of our narratives. I am thankful.

COLLECTIVE AFFIRMATION

YES! I ...

YES! I AM ...

a person
intelligent
human

YES! I CAN ...

do a kick-flip
identify almost every bird at the Arcata
Marsh
make great curry from scratch
wash my own clothes
WORK HARD

YES! I HAVE ...

courage

SÍ, YO SÉ QUE ...

mi familia es honrada
mi padre es bien trabajador
mi madre daría su vida por mí
soy humana y cometo errores
soy persona de color

YES! I KNOW ...

a lot about life because I have lived it

as a woman others plan my life, yet I know I can do what I want,

I will do what I want

CHANGE IS HARD

every all the little things that annoy my
brothers, so I keep on doing them

definitely, how to hit that snooze button

education is the most important thing, but so is Love and
Family

English and French fluently

no matter what, I will be ok

no one can force me to do anything

YES! I KNOW ...

nobody can tell me who I am nor who I should
be

not speaking Spanish does not define my race,
ethnicity, or identity

one day I will be able to repay my parents for their
support

SAN DIEGO LIKE THE BACK OF MY HAND

myself

sometimes I will make mistakes

tae Kwon Do

the lyrics to every song on the playlist someone
made for me

the only true measurement in the universe is
time

what a real family is

when we go out for dinner, people stare at us
because we are People of Color, but I also
know we do not care at all

YES! I KNOW ...

when you arrive at my abuelita's house there will be
food
where to go for help
WHO I AM ON MY OWN
who I want to help throughout my life
willow tree roots, when chewed, have the same effects as
aspirin

YES! I KNOW HOW ...

fortunate I am to have three siblings that love me and
support me
not to be perfect, and not being perfect makes me
exactly who I am

YES! I KNOW HOW TO ...

appreciate the little things in life
be a mother and also I know I do not have to be a mother
be courteous to others
be humble
be in a rush and how to be late
BE KIND
be strong
change a diaper
change my baby brother's diaper since I was 3 or 4 years old
cheer up my brother, my sister, my mom and my
dad

159

YES! I KNOW HOW TO ...

control my emotions just like my dad
dance the way my mother taught me
do my makeup in five minutes when I know the bus leaves in 10
find love, and how to ruin love
have fun anywhere, anytime
HELP SOMEONE
kick a soccer ball hard just like my sister
learn
listen to others
love my family

YES! I KNOW HOW TO ...

love others and respect them for who they are
love unconditionally
make enchiladas just like my mom's
make huevos rancheros
make love last
MAKE SOME BOMB-ASS ENCHILADAS, NOT GOING TO LIE
make the best of every situation
make the people I love smile
pay my bills on time
play soccer like a Mexican

YES! I KNOW HOW TO ...

respect everyone's decisions
sleep
smile, although I hate my smile
speak Spanish, mira--sé cómo bailar hasta que mis pies
se cansen
spend money on food even though I know I should be
saving up
WASH MY OWN CLOTHES
work as hard as my father does
write a good essay

YES! I KNOW I ...

can call my tía if I ever need anything
can't solve every single problem in the world
don't have to give my parents nietos, not
now, not soon, not ever
have a beautiful life
have a lot more to learn
KNOW
Love
LOVE THE RAIN BUT I HATE GETTING SOAKED
love to help others
only love pumpkin pie when it's piled with whipped cream

YES! I KNOW I ...

want to be a mother and one day I will

YES! I KNOW I AM ...

a smart, intelligent individual
beautiful
better than my past mistakes
blessed
free and I am wild
good enough
INDEPENDENT AND WILL ALWAYS BE
loved
loved, supported, and accepted by my family
more than a girl waiting to be married and supported

YES! I KNOW I AM ...

more than hips for carrying babies
more than the things I know
not docile
not perfect
not quiet
smarter than others think I am
STRONG
stronger than I look
successful already
willing to learn from my mistakes

YES! I KNOW I WILL ...

always put my family first
be a loving mother, and being a mother will
not be all I am
never change for anyone
never give up
travel to find my roots one day
try and try again

YES! I KNOW IF YOU ...

ASK MY DAD ENOUGH TIMES HE'LL EVENTUALLY GIVE IN
AND GET YOU WHAT YOU WANT

go to CVS with my dad when he buys beer he'll buy you something too

lick a cut your saliva will help heal the wound faster

make a funny face to a child, they'll laugh

YES! I KNOW IT IS ...

all possible

okay to not have it all together sometimes.

really hard to say "bubble" in an angry way

okay to be angry

okay to cry

YES! I KNOW MY ...

family loves to talk out loud

ABC'S BACKWARDS

abuelita puts her coin purse in her bra

family will always be there

culture

dad hides his chocolates in his underwear drawer

family loves and cares for me

family's history

family's struggles

feelings are valid

YES! I KNOW MY ...

mom doesn't really like my dad still plays futbol after his injury, but doesn't say anything because she knows how much the sport means to him

MOTHER IS SENSITIVE

parents struggle a lot, and their struggles are for my brothers and I

YES! I KNOW SOME ...

magic tricks

really good jokes

women do not want to be mothers and that is fine

YES! I KNOW WHAT ...

family means

I need to do when I go to work everyday

I want in life

I'd name my daughter if I had one and also what I'd name my son

it feels like to be ostracized by my own 'raza' and 'familia'

IT IS LIKE TO LOOK BETWEEN THE COUCH CUSHIONS AND UNDER THE CAR SEATS HOPING TO FIND ENOUGH QUARTERS TO BUY A GALLON OF MILK.

to say, and when to say it

YES! I KNOW WHAT IT'S LIKE TO ...

have a good time

lose a loved one

be up at 2 a.m. studying for a test I have in a couple of hours

not have a home

Works Cited

In Journal's Genesis

Acevedo, Luz A. Telling to Live: Latina Feminist Testimonios. Durham: Duke University Press, 2001.

Anzaldúa, Gloria. Borderlands: The New Mestiza = La Frontera. San Francisco: Aunt Lute Books, 2012.

Anzaldúa, Gloria and Cherríe Moraga. This Bridge Called My Back: Writings by Radical Women of Color. Watertown, Mass.: Persephone Press, 1983.

Cisneros, Sandra. A House of My Own: Stories from My Life. New York: Alfred A. Knopf, 2015.

In Editor's Introduction

Martínez, Demetria. Mother Tongue. New York: One World Ballantine Books, 1994

Made in the USA
San Bernardino, CA
20 April 2017